JN084901

TOBIRA II: Beginning Japanese Workbook 1
−Kanji, Reading, Writing

First published 2023

Kurosio Publishers
4-3, Nibancho, Chiyoda-ku, Tokyo 102-0084, Japan

ISBN 978-4-87424-960-4
Printed in Japan

TOBIRA
BEGINNING JAPANESE

初級日本語

とびら Ⅱ

ワークブック❶

漢字(かんじ)|読(よ)む|書(か)く

WORKBOOK 1
Kanji | Reading | Writing

[著者] 岡まゆみ Mayumi Oka　近藤純子 Junko Kondo　榊原芳美 Yoshimi Sakakibara　西村裕代 Hiroyo Nishimura　[監修] 筒井通雄 Michio Tsutsui

Kurosio Publishers

はじめに

本書は『初級日本語とびらI』で学んだことを基礎に、『初級日本語とびらII』で学ぶ漢字と漢字語彙を練習・強化し、日本語を読む力と書く力をさらに高めるためのワークブックです。本書には多様な形式の練習問題に加えて、多読や漢字ミーム(meme)、日本の歌などのコラムもあり、これらを通して身に付けた漢字語彙とその知識を活用することができます。

本書の主な特徴は次の通りです。

- 「各課のとびら」を通して、日本の文化や言語景観について知ることができる。
- 日本文化を随所に織り込んだ様々な練習問題を通して、単調になりがちな漢字学習が楽しく進められる。
- 「漢字の練習」では注意点が分かりやすく提示されているので、正しくきれいな字が書けるように練習できる。
- 練習問題の難易度は３段階で示されており、段階的に学習することができる。
- 字形・字音・字義を意識させる多様な練習問題を通して、漢字の形、読み方、意味、用法などを統合的に学習することができる。
- 学んだ漢字を総合的に復習するために、『初級日本語とびらI』の漢字総復習と、３課ごとの漢字復習のページが ある。
- 「読む練習」では文構造や内容理解を問う問題を通して、読み物をより正確に深く読む訓練をすると同時に、読み物を通して考える力を養うことができる。
- 後半の読む練習では一部、生教材を採用し、中級レベルへのスムーズな橋渡しとなる練習に取り組めるようになっている。
- 「書く練習」では本書独自のワークシートを活用することで、情報や自分の考えを自分の言葉で伝える文章構成力、表現力、創造力を養うことができる。
- 豊富なイラストや写真に加えて、二色刷りで紙面が見やすく魅力的である。

本書は授業での練習、宿題や小テスト、復習、自主学習など様々な場面や用途に活用できます。

本書作成にあたっては、平川ワイター永子さんの緻密で行き届いた校閲・校正作業と的確なアドバイスや提案に大いに助けられました。また、ロビン・グリフィンさんにはいつも迅速、的確に英語校正・翻訳をしていただきました。お二人のご尽力とご協力に深く感謝いたします。

最後に、くろしお出版編集部の市川麻里子さんには本書の制作全般にわたって大変お世話になりました。大変なスケジュールの中、本書編集のために日々、奮闘・尽力してくださったこと、感謝の念に耐えません。市川さんの優れた編集のおかげで、学習者が楽しみながら学べる日本語練習教材を完成することができました。ここに改めてお礼申し上げます。

2023年11月　著者一同

CONTENTS

How to use this workbook

このワークブックの使い方

The following is an overview of the organization and contents of this workbook.

■ Structure of each lesson

■ 各課の構成

各課のとびら Lesson preview → 漢字の練習 Kanji practice  読む練習 Reading practice → 書く練習 Writing practice

■ Lesson preview

- This page introduces the characters to be practiced in the given lesson, as well as fun activities, graphics, and more. Before moving on to the practice problems, check out this page for a preview of the characters you'll be studying.
- Lessons with Kanji practice sections include both an Entry Check and Exit Check. Use the Entry Check to mark which kanji you know how to read and write (○), which you recognize but cannot yet read and write (△), and which you don't know at all (×). After completing the practice problems, use the Exit Check to confirm whether you have learned the kanji for that lesson. Mark those you can now read and write, and review practice problems for unlearned kanji as needed.

■ Kanji practice

Kanji practice for each lesson begins with learning how to write each character introduced, then moves to reading the characters in context.

- In practicing character form, trace the gray guiding lines while following the given stroke order and stroke types (stop, flick, etc.).
- Then, using the model as a guide, write the kanji twice as neatly as possible in the two empty boxes. If you need more practice, use a notebook or separate sheet of paper to continue writing each character.

The difficulty of each practice problem is marked with a number of ★ s:

★ = basic
★★ = sentence-level
★★★ = practical application

Practice problems include opportunities to solve kanji puzzles, break down the elements that make up each kanji, learn the proper way to write each kanji and provide its *okurigana*, work with "The Story of Kanji" sections of the main textbook, and other ways to put what you've learned into practice. These exercises

このワークブックは次のような構成と内容になっています。

■ 各課のとびら

- 各課で導入する漢字に関係した楽しい情報やクイズ、これらの漢字が実際に使われている画像などがあります。練習を始める前に、どんな漢字を学ぶか見てみましょう。
- 各課のとびらには Entry Check と Exit Check があります。Entry Check ではその漢字を読んで書くことができたら○、どちらか一方だったら△、全然知らなかったら×を入れます。Exit Check ではその課の漢字がマスターできたかどうかチェックします。読み書きどちらもできるようになっていたら、○を入れてください。まだできていなければ、その漢字をもう一度練習しましょう。

■ 漢字の練習

各課の漢字の練習は字形の練習から始まり、漢字の読み書きの練習へと続きます。

- まず、字形練習は、漢字の書き順やトメ、ハネなどを見ながらグレーの線をなぞります。
- 次に、手本の漢字を見ながら、できる限り丁寧にバランスが整った漢字を二回書きます。ここでは二回だけ書くことになっていますが、ノートなど他の紙に何度も練習するといいでしょう。

各問にある★の数は難易度を表します。

★ ＝基本練習・単語レベルの練習
★★ ＝文レベルの練習
★★★ ＝応用練習

漢字の練習にはクイズのような練習、漢字を構成する部首や正しい字形や送りがなを学ぶ練習、『とびら II』の「漢字の話」に関連した練習など、様々な問題形式があるので、楽しく練習できます。また、その課の新しい漢字語彙だけでなく、既習の漢字も問題に入っているので、それらを繰り返し練習できます。最後は漢字を使ってまとまった

cover not only new kanji words and compounds from that lesson, but also those from past lessons for better repetition and retention. Finally, the end of the lesson moves beyond just reading and writing each character, providing a space to practice writing full sentences while using kanji in context.

文を書く練習があり、単に漢字だけを「読む・書く」だけでなく、漢字を「文脈の中で使う」練習もできるようになっています。

■ Reading practice

Reading practice corresponds to the "Reading" segments of *TOBIRA II* (intensive reading). Read the passages from the main textbook, then write your answers in your workbook. Note that some sections may vary from those listed in the main textbook.

■ 読む練習

読む練習には『とびらII』の「読みましょう」のセクション2（精読）の質問の部分が載っています。教科書の読み物を読んで、解答を書き込んでください。一部、教科書とは異なる部分や教科書には載っていない問題もあります。

■ Writing practice

Writing practice provides a space to practice writing full compositions on various topics, while also expanding on content presented in Reading practice. First, use the "Prewriting activity" worksheet to collect your thoughts and organize information. Using this worksheet will give your ideas more clarity, allowing you to write more cohesive essays. Then, using the grammar, vocabulary, and kanji learned for that lesson, draft your essay from your outline. Presenting your finished essay in class or posting it on social media are great ways to share your ideas with others. Worksheets are available for download via the Workbook section of the *TOBIRA* website below.

■ 書く練習

書く練習は読む練習の内容を発展させた活動で、様々な内容についてまとまりのある文章を書く練習です。まずPre-writing activityのワークシートを使って考えや情報を整理し、書く内容を準備してください。このワークシートを使用することで、何を書くか明確になり、まとまりのある文が書きやすくなります。次に、その課で習った文法や単語、漢字を使いながら、まとめたことを文で書きましょう。書けたら、是非クラス内で発表したり、SNSで発信したりして、色々な人と共有してください。ワークシートは「とびら初級WEBサイト」の「ワークブックエリア」からダウンロードできます。

■ Columns and Kanji Review

- These columns introduce topics for further study in the form of extensive reading exercises, memes, Japanese songs, and more.
- Review pages provide a space to revisit and practice kanji learned over the last three sections.

■ コラムと漢字復習ページ

- 多読、ミーム、日本の歌などについてのコラムがあるので、参考にしてください。
- 復習ページでは、3課ごとに漢字の復習練習ができるようになっていますので、活用してください。

■ Answer sheets

Answers can be written in and submitted directly from the workbook, though the same answer sheets are available for download via the Workbook section of the *TOBIRA* website below.

■ 解答用紙について

解答は本冊に書き込んで切り取って提出することができますが、解答用紙を下の「とびら初級WEBサイト」の「ワークブックエリア」からダウンロードすることもできます。

tobirabeginning.9640.jp/workbook/

■ Answer keys

Instructors can access answer keys by registering through the Instructor Resources section of the *TOBIRA* website. An electronic version can otherwise be purchased and viewed separately.

■ 解答について

解答は「とびら初級WEBサイト」の「教師エリア」に登録するとご覧になれます。登録教師以外の方は別売の電子版をご覧ください。

私に漢字の覚え方を教えてくれない？
Can you teach me how to memorize kanji?

Kanji List できるCheck ✓

	140	141	142	143	144	145	146	147	148	149	150	151	152	153	154	155	156	157 (E6)	158 (E7)
Kanji	勉	強	着	自	場	所	茶	料	理	肉	鳥	魚	絵	例	方	次	最	王	糸
Entry Check																			
Exit Check																			

Kanji elements with meanings

Eight elements that appear in this lesson's kanji

Kanji in images with meanings

Kanji in daily life

Which kanji can you recognize?

Class: __________ Name: ________________________

漢字の練習 | Kanji practice

1 Trace the gray kanji first, then write each kanji twice as neatly as possible.

S=stop F=flick R=release C=curved line ↓→=direction ○=note ◌=space

140 勉 (Elongate to cover 力)

141 強 (one stroke)

142 着

143 自 (Slant downward)

144 場 (Slant upward)

145 所

146 茶

147 料

148 理 (Slant upward)

149 肉

150 鳥

151 魚

Class: __________ Name: ____________________

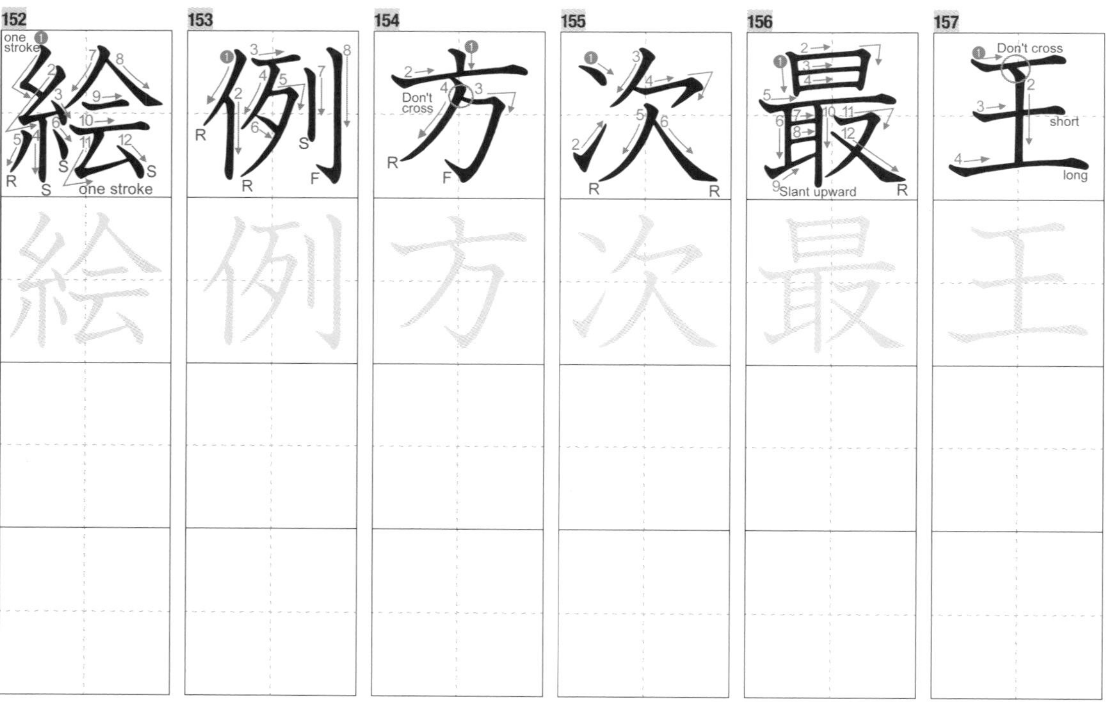

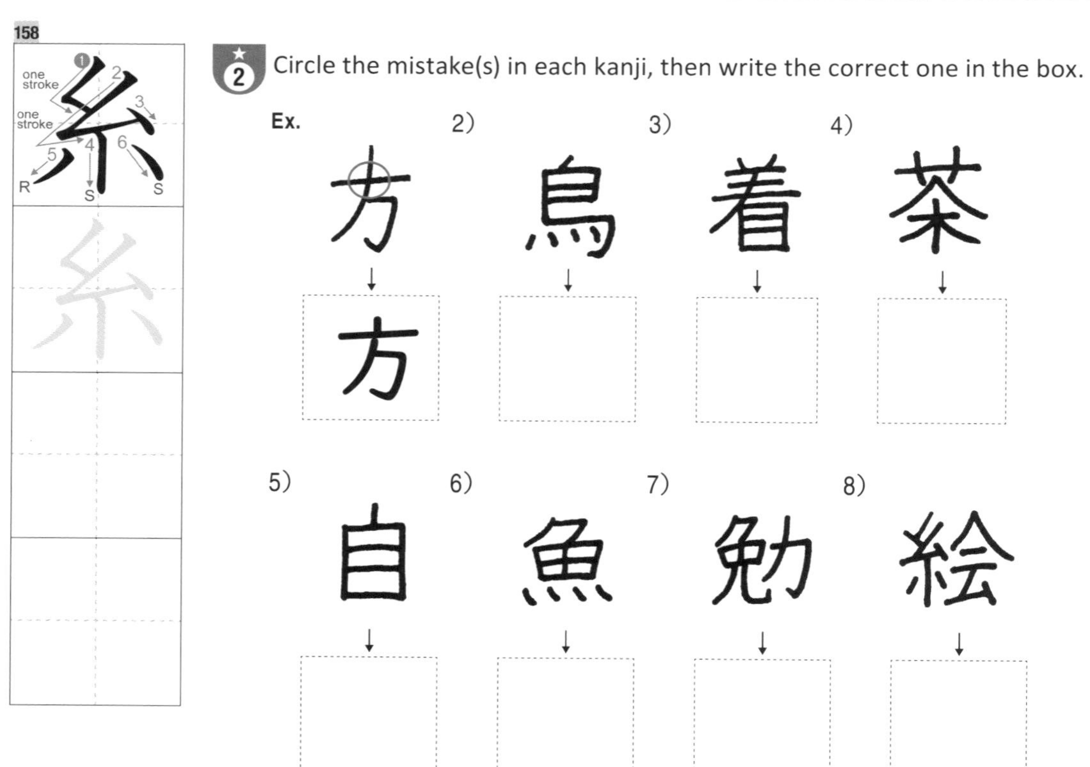

2 Circle the mistake(s) in each kanji, then write the correct one in the box.

Ex. 方 → 方

2） 鳥

3） 着

4） 茶

5） 自

6） 魚

7） 勉

8） 絵

Class: ______ Name: ______

3 Complete kanji and kanji compounds 1)-7) by adding an element from the box below. Then, provide the reading for each word in ( ) and its meaning in __.

4 For each picture, write the corresponding kanji or kanji compound in the box, then provide its reading in ( ).

Class: __________ Name: ______________________

5 Make kanji compounds by combining one kanji each from A and B below. Then, write the words in ◯◯ and their readings in __.

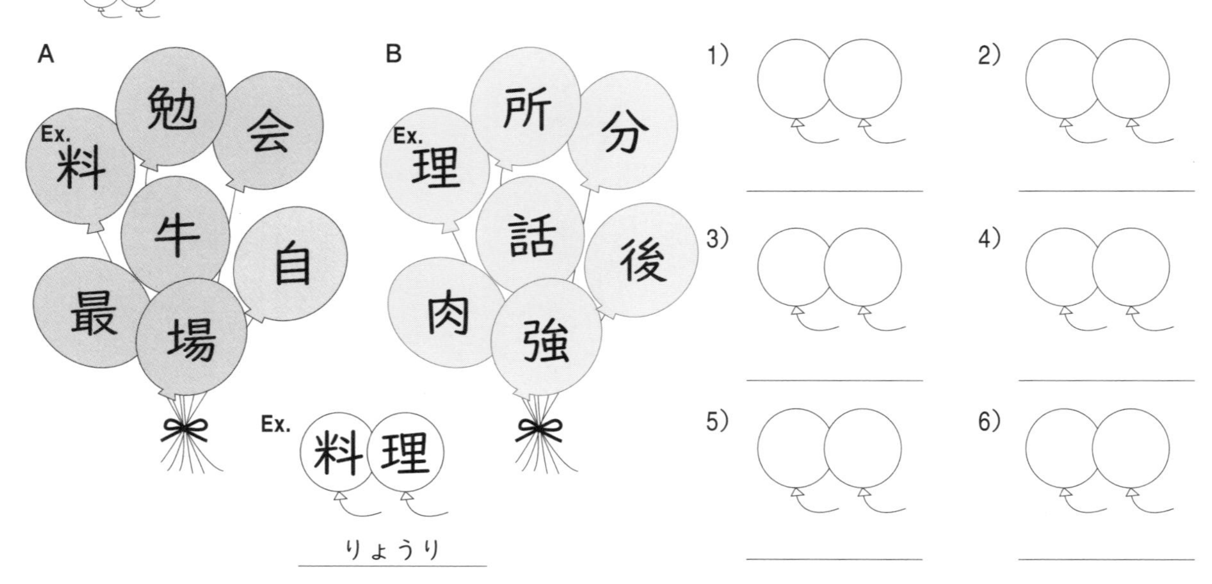

6 You are texting with Ai about studying kanji. Provide the readings for the kanji of the underlined words.

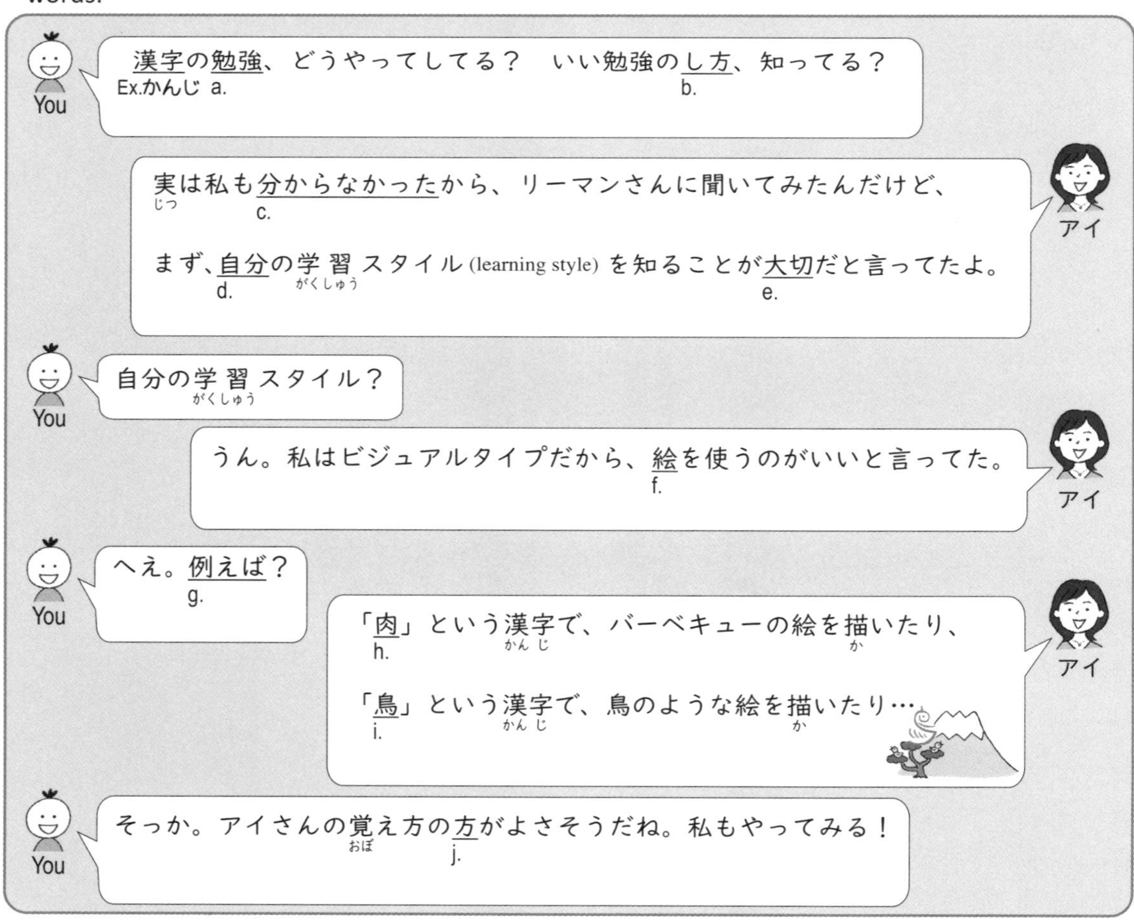

Class: __________ Name: ______________________

7 (★★) Read 漢字(かんじ)の話 on p.24 of *TOBIRA II*, then choose a kanji from A to fill in each box and complete the kanji compounds as in the example. Each word should be read in the direction that the arrow indicates. Then, choose the reading for each word from B.

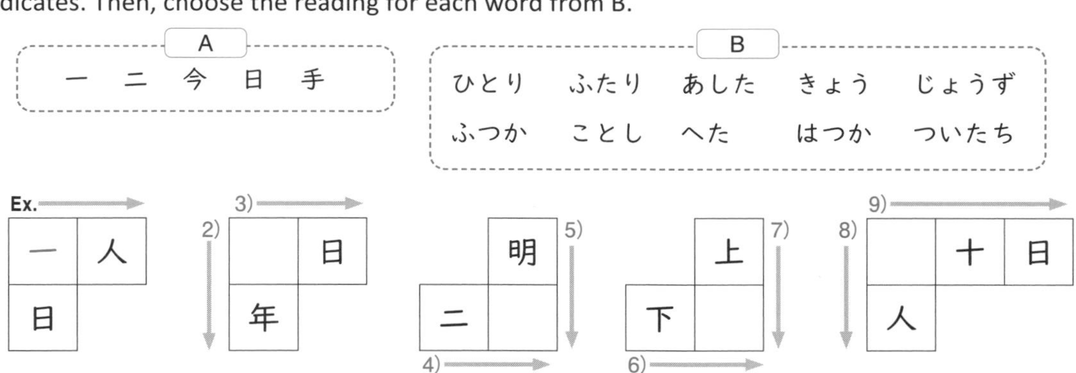

Ex. ひとり　　2) ______　　4) ______　　6) ______　　8) ______

1) ______　　3) ______　　5) ______　　7) ______　　9) ______

8 (★★) Provide the readings for the kanji of the underlined words. Note that the same kanji may have different readings depending on how it is used.

Ex. 牛肉は牛の肉です。
ぎゅうにく　うし　にく

1) 駅(えき)に何時に着きますか(a.)。外は寒(さむ)いから、コートを着て(b.)くださいね。

2) 山下公園(こうえん)はとてもいい所(a.)です。場所(b.)を教(おし)えますから、行ってみてください。

hair donation

3) 大切(a.)な髪(かみ)を切って(b.)、ヘアドネーションをしました。

4) 自分(a.)の好きな料理のレシピを書いてください。時間は三十分(b.)です。

分からない(c.)単語(たんご)は辞書(じしょ)で調(しら)べてもいいです。

5) 今日、会話(a.)の授業(じゅぎょう)で日本語をたくさん練習(れんしゅう)しました。

その後で、日本人の友達に会って(b.)、日本語をたくさん話しました(c.)。

6) 昨日(きのう)は風(かぜ)がとても強かったです(a.)。こわくて勉強できませんでした(b.)。

7) ここにくつを入れて(a.)ください。

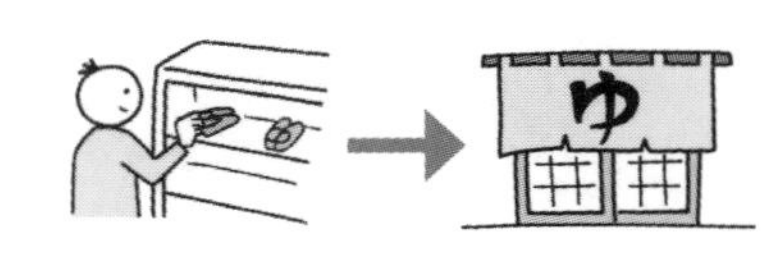

それから、あのドアから中に入って(b.)ください。

Lesson 11

Class: __________ Name: ______________________

9 ★★ Provide the kanji for the underlined hiragana words. Add *okurigana* as necessary. The numbers in ( ) indicate the total number of kanji that should be provided.

父のスパイスカレー

1) 父はりょうり(a.)がじょうず(b.)です。パンやケーキもじぶん(c.)でつくります。先週はインドのスパイスカレーをつくりました。私もてつだいました(d.)。(7)

2) スパイスカレーのつくりかた(a.)は、まず、やさいを小さく切って、なべでいためます。つぎに(b.)、なべに水とトマトをいれます(c.)。それから、とりにく(d.)とヨーグルトをまぜたものをいれます。ぎゅうにく(e.)やさかな(f.)をつかって(g.)もいいです。(10)

3) 私たちはスパイスカレーをたくさんつくったから、つぎ(a.)の日はトンカツ (pork cutlet) をのせて、カツカレーにしました。さいご(b.)にカレーうどんにして食べました。(3)

トンカツ

4) インドやネパールのスパイスカレーは、今いろいろなところ(a.)で食べることができます。私たちはインドのチャイというおちゃ(b.)も好きで、よく飲みます。(2)

カレーうどん

チャイ

10 ★★ Provide the readings for kanji words a.-e. in __. Then, fill in ( ) with the corresponding letter of the most appropriate word to complete each sentence.

a. 最後に __________ b. 次に __________ c. 入れます __________

d. 切って __________ e. 作り方 __________

卵(たまご)サンド (egg sandwich) の作り方

今日はおいしくて簡単(かんたん)な卵(たまご)サンドの 1)( ) を説明(せつめい)します。まず、レタスを洗(あら)います。2)( )、卵(たまご)をゆでて、小さく 3)( )、ボウル (bowl) に 4)( )。それから、塩(しお)をかけて、ドレッシングとまぜます。5)( )、パンにレタスと卵(たまご)をはさんでください。おいしい卵(たまご)サンドのできあがりです！

11 ★★★ Using #10 as a model, write your own simple recipe for a tasty dish. Use kanji that you have learned in LL3-11 as much as possible.

Class: ________ Name: ____________

読む練習(れんしゅう) | Reading practice

▶『とびら II』L11#2(p.48)を見て、やってください。

リーマンさんが作った「にゃんたはどこ？」というなぞときの問題(もんだい)を読んで、質問(しつもん)に答(こた)えましょう。

Identifying noun modification clauses

1) Write the part that modifies each noun in boxes a.-f.

l.2 a. ____________ なぞときの問題(もんだい)

l.6 b. ____________ 時

l.8 c. ____________ 人

l.11 d. ____________ 物

l.13 e. ____________ 時

l.13 f. ____________ 所

Understanding demonstratives: そ-words

2) What do the その+noun combinations ①-③ in the passage refer to? Rewrite the phrases by identifying the referents.

l.2 ① その解(と)き方＝____________解(と)き方

l.19 ② その絵　＝____________絵

l.20 ③ その読み方＝____________読み方

Comprehension check

3) 全部(ぜんぶ)読んでから、次の質問(しつもん)に答(こた)えてください。

a. 問題(もんだい)１の答(こた)えは何ですか。 ____________

b. 問題(もんだい)２の答(こた)えは何ですか。 ____________

c. 問題(もんだい)３の答(こた)えは何ですか。 ____________

d. どれがリーマンさんが描(か)いた絵だと思いますか。 ________

(1)

(2)

(3)

(4)

e. 問題(もんだい)４の答(こた)えは何ですか。 ____________

4)「にゃんたはどこ？」のなぞときは、どうでしたか。コメントを書きましょう。

____

____

____

Class: __________ Name: ______________________

書く練習 | Writing practice

▶書くシートは「とびら初級WEBサイト」にあります。

Create a なぞとき (riddle) problem

Task: Try your hand at creating a なぞとき problem like「にゃんたはどこ？」in #2 on p.48 of *TOBIRA II*.

1 **Pre-writing activity:** Find some ideas on the internet for your なぞとき problem using the following suggestions.

- Search keywords: 謎解きクイズ　小学生 etc.
- Websites:「謎解き王国」「なぞまっぷ」etc.

You may also search for "riddles for kids" in your own language.

2 **Writing:** Write a なぞとき problem and its answer in Japanese. You may include a drawing if necessary. Avoid using translation tools such as AI chat bots and translation functions.

Checklist

✓	Use the です・ます forms.
✓	Write at least two sentences for the problem and three sentences for the answer.
✓	If uncertain about the correct katakana spelling of a proper name, write it in katakana and provide the English equivalent above. Do the same in the following lessons.
✓	Use the following: ☐ noun modification clauses ☐ 答えは～です。～からです。(in providing the answer)
✓	Use as many learned kanji as possible.

3 **Post-writing activity:** Share your なぞとき with your classmates and challenge them to solve it.

Exit Check

Now go back to the Kanji List for this lesson (p.6) and do the exit check to see what kanji you can read and write.

Class: __________ Name: ______________________

『とびらⅠ』の漢字の復習 | TOBIRA I Kanji Review

➡ 『とびらⅠ』の3課から10課の漢字の言葉です。覚えていますか。読んでみましょう。

1 Numbers and counters

一　二　三　四　五　六　七　八　九　十　百　千　万　～円　～番　～度　～回　～人

2 Time

今日　明日　毎日　時間　午前　午後　［月・火・水・木・金・土・日］曜日　週末　先週
今週　来週　毎週　先月　今月　来月　毎月　今年　来年　毎年　今　昔　後で
～分　～時　～時間　～日　～月　～年

3 School

学生　先生　～年生　学校　大学　高校　日本語　英語　外国語　作文

4 Weather and nature

天気　雨　雪　晴れ　花　山　川　海　田　日　月　水　木

5 People

人　日本人　私　友達　子ども　男の人　女の人　社長　作家　父・お父さん　母・お母さん
兄・お兄さん　姉・お姉さん　弟(さん)　妹(さん)　兄弟

6 Body-related

体　口　目　耳　手　足　元気(な)　病気

7 Places and locations

家　(お)寺　会社　道　町　国　外国　上　下　中　外　右　左　前　後ろ　間

8 Verbs

(～を)食べる　飲む　見る　聞く　読む　書く　持つ　作る　買う　売る　使う　出す　休む
知る | (～に)行く　来る　帰る　出かける　入る　住む | (～に／と)会う　話す | (～と)思う
言う | (～が)分かる　立つ

9 Adjectives

I-adjs.：大きい　小さい　新しい　古い　高い　安い　明るい　暗い　広い　早い　長い　楽しい　悪い
Na-adjs.：上手(な)　下手(な)　好き(な)　大好き(な)　有名(な)　親切(な)　大切(な)

10 Other nouns　何　名前　お金　音　食べ物　飲み物　買い物　気分　文化　音楽　文学　書道　新聞

➡ The following kanji have different readings depending on how they are used. Can you read all of the words below?

1) 日：［一・二・三・四・五・六・七・八・九・十］日　日曜日
一日 (one day)　今日　明日　いい日　日本
2) 月：月曜日　一月　来月　毎月
3) 今：今　今日　今週　今月　今年　今度
4) 人：いい人　一人　二人　三人　日本人　人気
5) 分：［一・二・三・四・五・六・七・八・九・十］分　何分　気分　分かる

Lesson 11

Lesson 12 今度日本に来たら、何がしたい？

When you come to Japan next time, what do you want to do?

Kanji List　できるCheck ☑

	159	160	161	162	163	164	165	166	167	168	169	170	171	172	173	174	175	176	177 (E8)
Kanji	集	配	動	働	走	当	荷	由	計	画	映	仕	事	初	東	京	同	半	士
Entry Check																			
Exit Check																			

A day in Tokyo　Can you tell what is going on in the picture?

Flyer for Tokyo sightseeing　Do you understand the tour schedule?

Class: __________ Name: ____________________

漢字の練習 | Kanji practice
かんじ れんしゅう

1 Trace the gray kanji first, then write each kanji twice as neatly as possible.

S=stop F=flick R=release C=curved line ↓→=direction ○=note ◌=space

159	160	161	162	163	164
集	配	動	働	走	当
1 2 3 4 5 6 7 8 9 10 11 12; Slant downward; R S R	1 2 3 4 5 6 7 8 9 10; C; separate strokes; F; C	1 2 3 4 5 6 7 8 9 10 11; Slant upward; F	1 2 3 4 5 6 7 8 9 10 11 12 13; R; Slant upward; F	1 2 3 4 5 6 7; separate strokes; R R	1 2 3 4 5 6; Don't cross
集	配	動	働	走	当

165	166	167	168	169	170
荷	由	計	画	映	仕
1 2 3 4 5 6 7 8 9 10; F	1 2 3 4 5	1 2 3 4 5 6 7 8 9	1 2 3 4 5 6 7 8; Don't cross; one stroke; S	1 2 3 4 5 6 7 8 9; R R	1 2 3 4 5; long; short
荷	由	計	画	映	仕

Class: __________ Name: ____________________

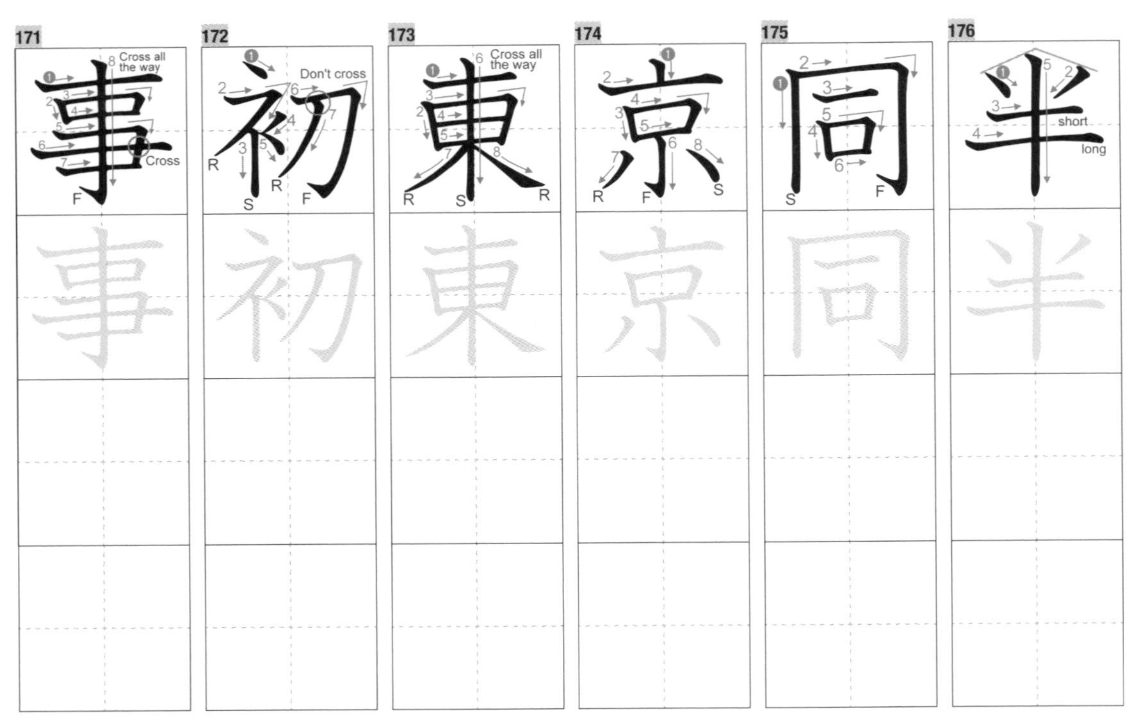

177

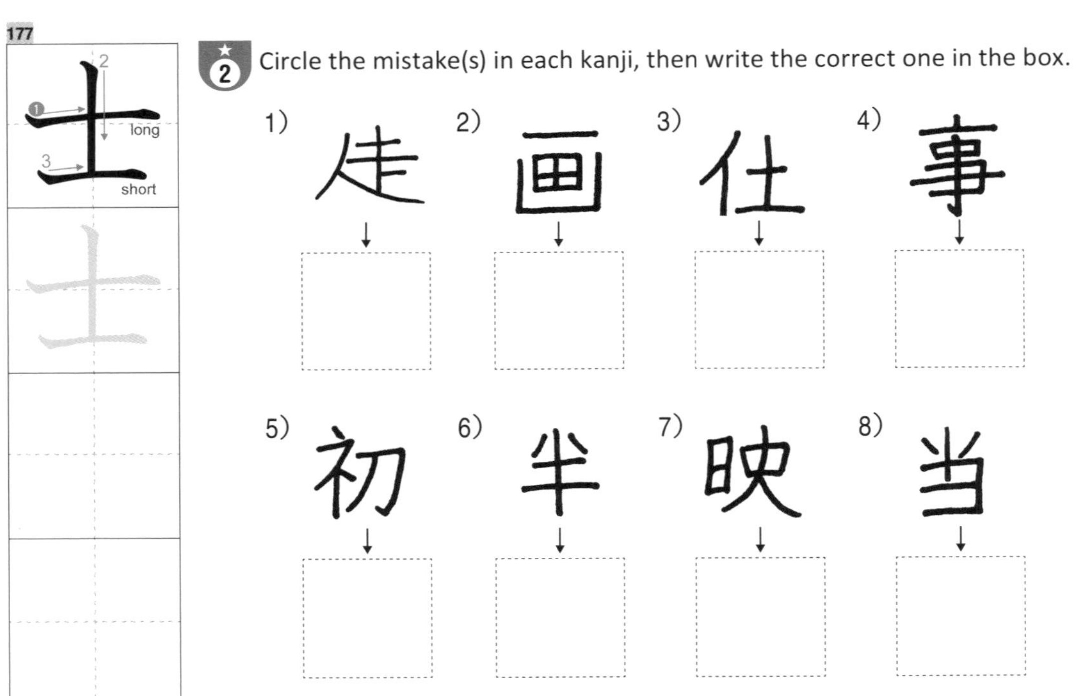

2 Circle the mistake(s) in each kanji, then write the correct one in the box.

1) 走　2) 画　3) 仕　4) 事

5) 初　6) 半　7) 映　8) 当

Class: ___________ Name: ______________________

3 Complete kanji and kanji compounds 1)-8) by adding an element from the box below. Then, provide the reading for each word in ( ) and its meaning in __.

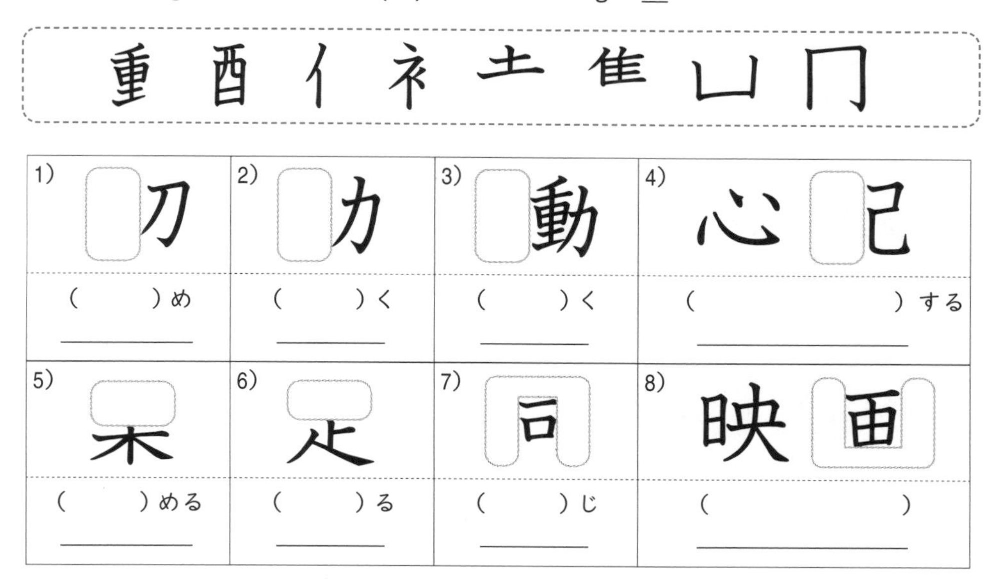

4 For each picture, write the corresponding kanji or kanji compound in the box, then provide its reading in ( ).

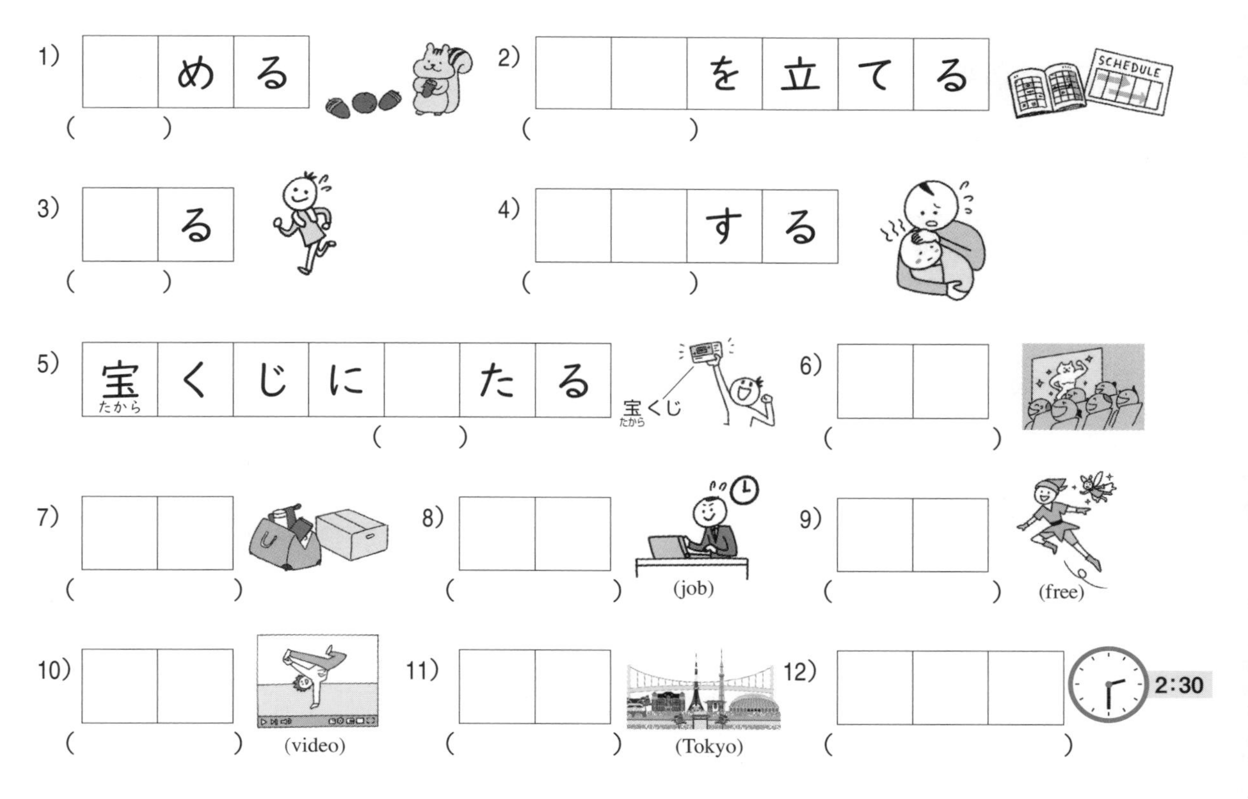

Class: ________ Name: ____________________

5 Circle the correct combination of kanji and its *okurigana*. Then, write its meaning in __.

Ex. [(a.) 宝(たから)くじに当たる　b. 宝(たから)くじに当る]　to win a lottery

1) [a. 初じめて　b. 初めて　c. 初て]　________

2) [a. 集つめる　b. 集める　c. 集る]　________

3) [a. 働たらく　b. 働らく　c. 働く]　________

4) [a. 動ごく　b. 動く]　________

5) [a. 走しる　b. 走る]　________

6 Choose a kanji from the list below to fill in each box and complete the following words. Each word should be read in the direction that the arrow indicates. Then, provide the reading for each word in __.

Kanji List: 画　物　事　生

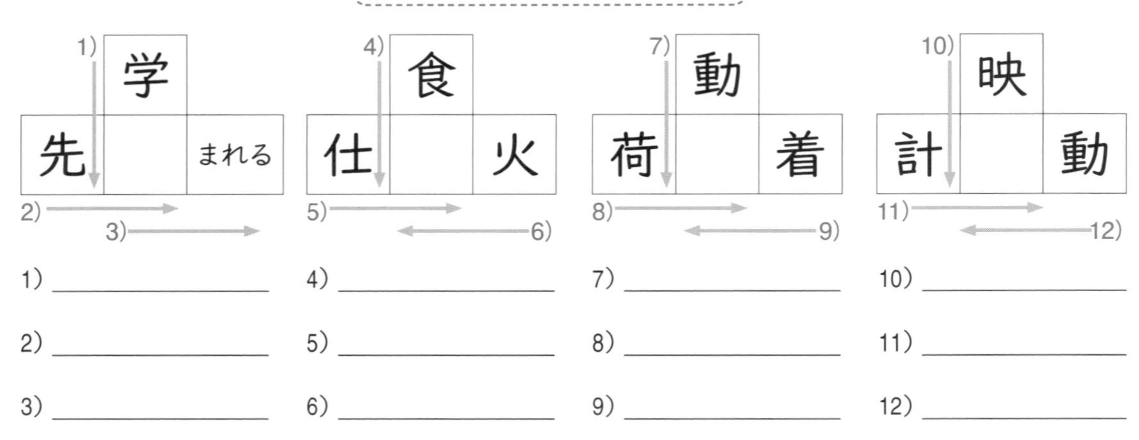

1) ________　4) ________　7) ________　10) ________

2) ________　5) ________　8) ________　11) ________

3) ________　6) ________　9) ________　12) ________

7 Provide the readings for words 1)-5) and underlined words 6)-8) in (　), then match each word with its explanation on the right as in the example.

Ex. 東京　(とうきょう)・　　・イヌやネコやパンダやコアラ

1) 動画　(　　　　)・　　・日本の首都(しゅと) (capital)

2) 子ども達　(　　　　)・　　・ビデオ

3) 親　(　　　　)・　　・朝(あさ)ご飯(はん)や昼(ひる)ご飯(はん)を食べること

4) 動物　(　　　　)・　　・働くこと

5) 自由　(　　　　)・　　・自分がしたいことができること

6) <u>仕事</u>をする　(　　　　)・　　・父か母か両親(りょうしん)

7) <u>食事</u>する　(　　　　)・　　・予定(よてい)を立てること

8) <u>計画</u>を立てる　(　　　　)・　　・二人以上(いじょう) (or more) の子ども

Class: ____________ Name: ____________________________

8 You dropped your kanji flash cards! Pick them up and organize them into six pairs of kanji compounds. Write the kanji in the boxes, the compounds' readings in (   ), and meanings in ___.

	Kanji words			Readings	Meanings
Ex.	時	+	計	(とけい)	watch; clock
1)		+		( )	______
2)		+		( )	______
3)		+		( )	______
4)		+		( )	______
5)		+		( )	______
6)		+		( )	______

物　仕　計　京　当　事　動　画　荷　東　配　時　本　心

9 Provide the readings for the following kanji words and compounds in ___. Then, fill in (   ) with the corresponding letter of the most appropriate word to complete each sentence.

Ex. a. 友達 ＿ともだち＿　b. 私達 ＿わたしたち＿

（ b ）は同じ授業(じゅぎょう)を取(と)っている時に、（ a ）になりました。

1) a. 動画 ＿＿＿＿　b. 動物 ＿＿＿＿　c. 動いている ＿＿＿＿

A：私は（　　）の（　　）を見るのが好きです。

B：私もです！　ジャンプしたりして（　　）ネコを見るのが好きです。

2) a. 親切 ＿＿＿＿　b. 親 ＿＿＿＿

私の（　　）はいつも「みんなに（　　）にしましょう」と言います。

3) a. 荷物 ＿＿＿＿　b. 買い物 ＿＿＿＿

たくさん（　　）をして（　　）が多(おお)くなったから、タクシーで家に帰った。

4) a. 大事 ＿＿＿＿　b. 仕事 ＿＿＿＿

A：熱(ねつ)があるから、今日は（　　）を休みます。

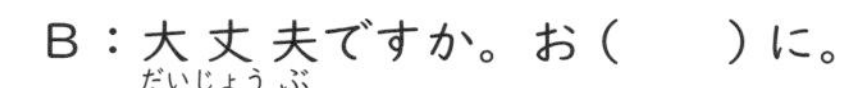

B：大丈夫(だいじょうぶ)ですか。お（　　）に。

Lesson 12

Class: __________ Name: ______________________

10 Provide the kanji for the underlined hiragana words. Add *okurigana* as necessary. The numbers in ( ) indicate the total number of kanji that should be provided.

私の旅行(りょこう)けいかく

1) 私はジョンさんの日本旅行(りょこう)の<u>どうが</u>(a.)を見て、<u>おなじ</u>(b.) <u>ところ</u>(c.)に行きたいと思いました。だから、旅行(りょこう)の<u>けいかく</u>(d.)を<u>たてました</u>(e.)。姉は<u>しごと</u>(f.)があるから、行けませんが、兄といっしょに行きます。(9)

2) まず、渋谷(しぶや)に行きます。成田空港(なりたくうこう)から渋谷駅(しぶやえき)まで電車(でんしゃ)で<u>いちじかんはん</u>(a.)ぐらいかかります。駅(えき)のコインロッカーに<u>にもつ</u>(b.)を<u>いれて</u>(c.)から、六本木(ろっぽんぎ)で<u>はたらいて</u>(d.)いる友達と会って、<u>しょくじ</u>(e.)をして、その後で、<u>えいが</u>(f.)を見に行きます。(12)

3) 私はマグネットを<u>あつめて</u>(a.)いるから、<u>とうきょう</u>(b.)でマグネットを買いたいです。それから、毎日ジョギングをしているから、人気がある皇居(こうきょ)ラン (Jogging around the Imperial Palace) に行って、<u>はしって</u>(c.)みたいです。(4)

4) <u>はじめて</u>(a.) 兄と<u>ふたり</u>(b.)で旅行(りょこう)するから、<u>おや</u>(c.)は<u>しんぱい</u>(d.)していますが、<u>じゆう</u>(e.)に好きなところに行けるから、私達は本当に<u>たのしみ</u>(f.)にしています。(9)

11 Using #10 as a model, write your own travel plans for going to Japan. Use kanji that you have learned in LL3-12 as much as possible.

Class: __________ Name: ____________________

読む練習 | Reading practice

▶『とびらII』L12#2(p.82)を見て、やってください。

科学者の野口英世の話を読んで、質問に答えましょう。

Recognizing event sequence

1) Based on the story, complete the following biographical timeline for Hideyo Noguchi.

年	才	主な出来事 (major events)
1876	0	いなかの貧乏な農家で生まれました。
	1才半	
		自分の左手について書いた作文を発表しました。
1900		
~		色々な病気の研究をして、病気の人達を助けました。
1928		

Understanding demonstratives: そ-words

2) What do the そ-words ①-③ in the passage refer to? Rewrite the phrases by identifying the referents.

l.17 ① それを ＝ ______________________________ を

l.19 ② その時 ＝ ______________________________ 時

l.27 ③ そのお金＝ ______________________________ お金

Summarizing

3) 野口はどんな人でしたか。いいことと悪いことについて、書いてください。

______________________ が、______________________ 。

☺ ☹

Comprehension check

4) In your textbook, underline the part of the text that modifies each noun in boxes a.-g.

5) Mark ○ if the statement is true and × if it is false.

( ) 野口は日本だけで有名だ。世界の人はあまり知らない。

( ) 野口は左手を手術した後で、医者になりたいと思った。

( ) 野口は研究が大好きで、全然遊ばなかったようだ。

( ) 野口はお金を使う前に、計画を立てる人だった。

6)「野口みたいな人がお札になった」(ll.30-31) ことについてどう思いますか。

____

Class: __________ Name: ____________________

書く練習(れんしゅう) | Writing practice

▶書くシートは「とびら初級(しょきゅう)WEBサイト」にあります。

Write a short essay about a person

Task: Write about a person who inspires you or makes you strive for self-improvement. Support your selection with episodes that would make your readers want to know more about that person.

1 Pre-writing activity: Brainstorm your ideas about「私がすごいと思う人」and create an outline using simple keywords or phrases in Japanese. (Do not write full sentences.)

① すごいと思う人は？	② 理由(りゆう)や例	③ 最後に
・それはだれ？ ・どんな人？(Exs. profession, achievements)	・どうしてすごいと思う？ ・すごいと思う例やエピソード (anectode)	・もし____たら、どうする？ (What will you do?) ・いっしょに何がしたい？

2 Writing: Based on the outline above, write about the person of your choice. Expand your ideas by adding interesting facts, details, and more thoughts.

Checklist

✓	Use the です・ます forms.
✓	Organize factual information and your thoughts logically. Write at least six sentences, organized into two or more paragraphs.
✓	Support your points with facts, reasons, and examples.
✓	Use as many learned kanji as possible.
✓	Use as many grammar points as possible from the box below.

☐ Potential forms of verbs ☐ V 前に ☐ V 後で ☐ ～たら
☐ ～みたい／よう ☐ ～ておく ☐ ～時 ☐ Noun modification clauses

Now go back to the Kanji List for this lesson (p.16) and do the exit check to see what kanji you can read and write.

COLUMN

1

ミーム (meme) で漢字にチャレンジ！

みなさんは漢字が好きですか。ミームを作って漢字で遊んでみませんか。（『とびら II』Unit4 チャレンジ #3 (p.120) を見てください）

■ ミームを作る前に

① ミームの例

色々な漢字のミームの例があります。どれがおもしろいと思いますか。

〈例〉

1)

2)

3)

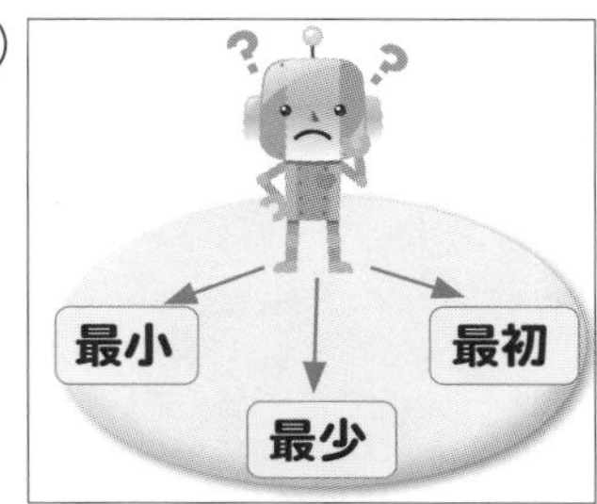

4)

5)

② ブレインストーミング

1) よく間違える漢字、よく忘れる漢字は何ですか。たくさん考えてみましょう。

2) おもしろいと思う漢字や変だと思う漢字は何ですか。

3) 好きな漢字やきらいな漢字は何ですか。

■ ミームを作る

上の①と②をもとに (based on)、色々な漢字のミームを作ってシェアしてみましょう。

Lesson 12

Lesson 13 明日行ってみようと思います。

I think I'll go tomorrow.

Kanji List できるCheck ☑

	178	179	180	181	182	183	184	185	186	187	188	189	190	191	192	193	194	195	196
Kanji	拾	返	守	変	止	電	車	神	様	注	意	味	色	々	世	界	記	昨	若
Entry Check																			
Exit Check																			

Kanji story Can you tell which new kanji the following kanji stories represent? (Refer to 漢字(かんじ) on pp.92-94 of *TOBIRA II* if necessary.)

1)

Benjamin Franklin discovered it using a kite in the rain.

2)

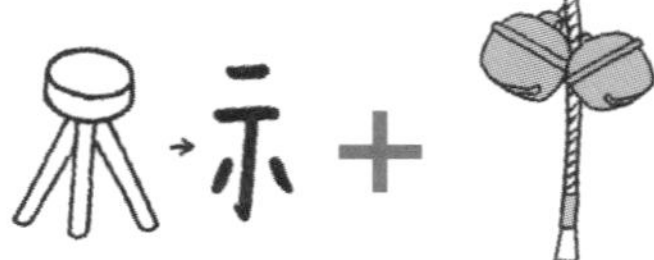

This small table is used to place offerings to god.

This bell can be seen in shrines.

3)

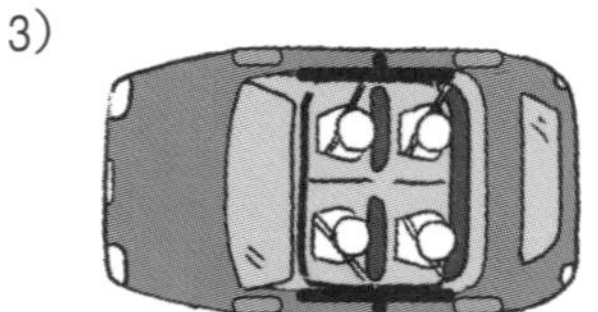

This machine has wheels.

4)

The police officer stops cars for a pedestrian.

5)

The words are recorded in the notebook.

6)

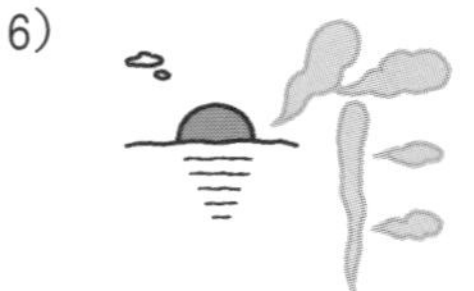

The day is done.

7)

I return this.

Kanji in daily life Which kanji can you recognize?

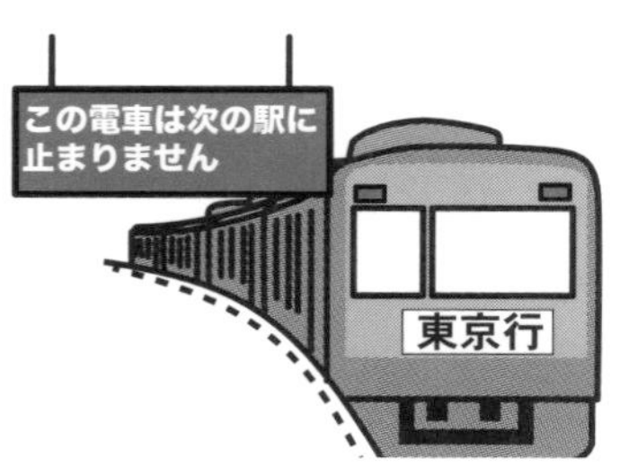

Class: ____________ Name: ____________________________

漢字（かんじ）の練習（れんしゅう） | Kanji practice

1 Trace the gray kanji first, then write each kanji twice as neatly as possible.

S=stop F=flick R=release C=curved line ↓ → =direction ◯=note ◌=space

178	179	180	181	182	183
拾	返	守	変	止	電
拾	返	守	変	止	電

184	185	186	187	188	189
車	神	様	注 (short / long)	意	味 (short / long)
車	神	様	注	意	味

Lesson 13

Class: __________ Name: ______________________

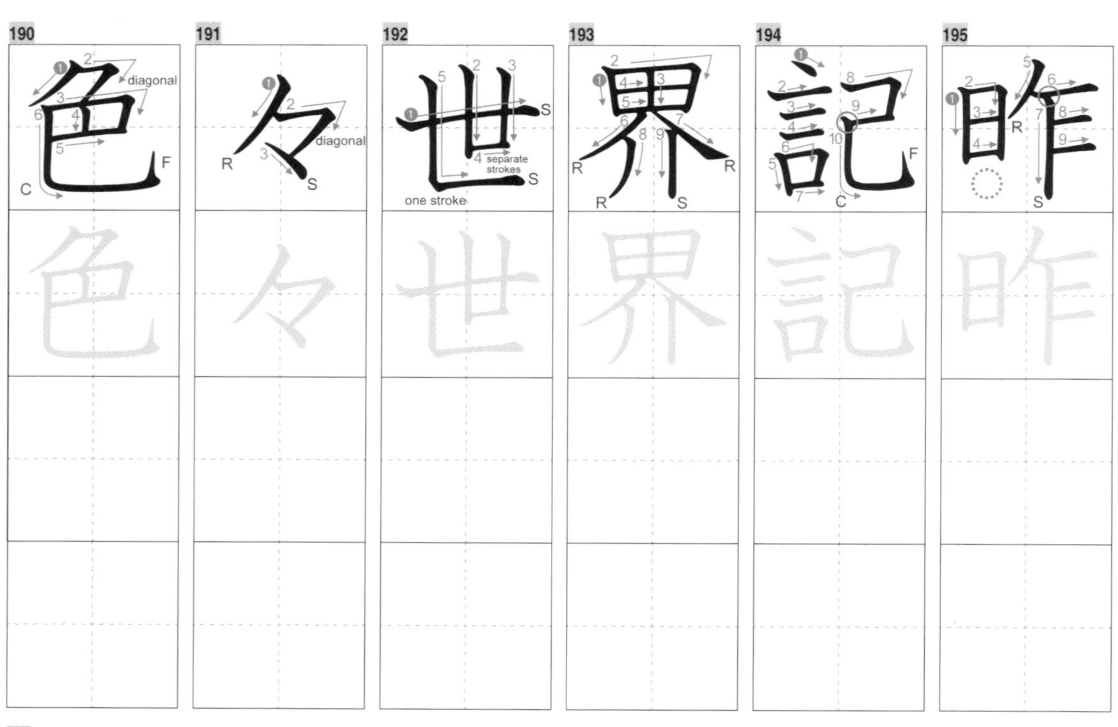

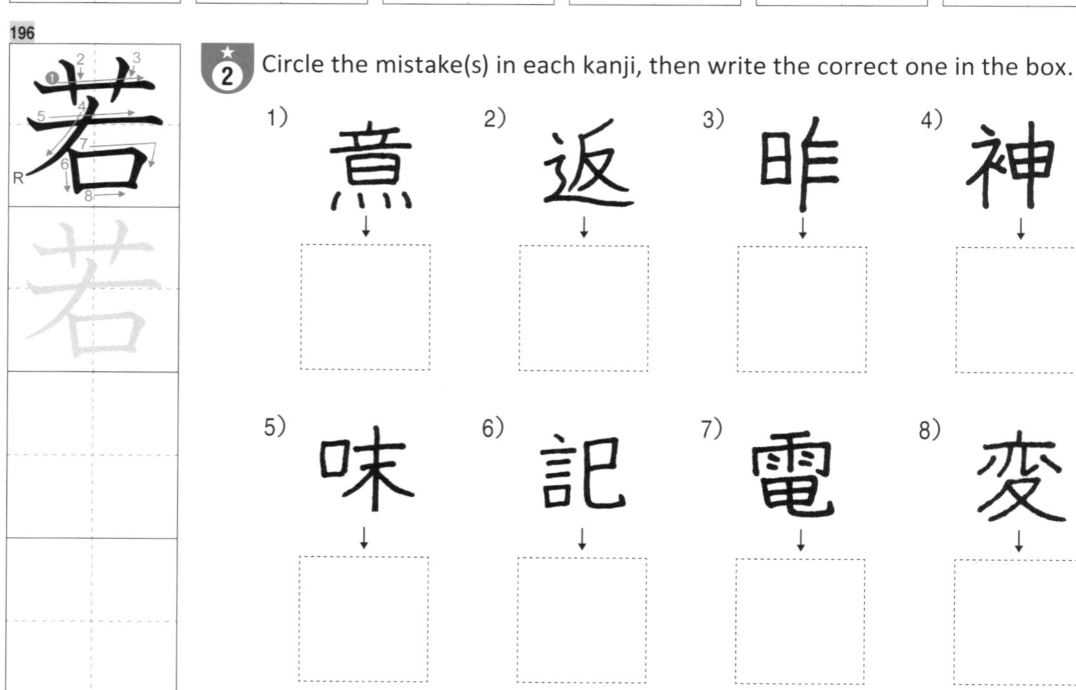

2 Circle the mistake(s) in each kanji, then write the correct one in the box.

3 For each kanji, mark the correct one with ✓, then circle the mistake(s) in the other ones.

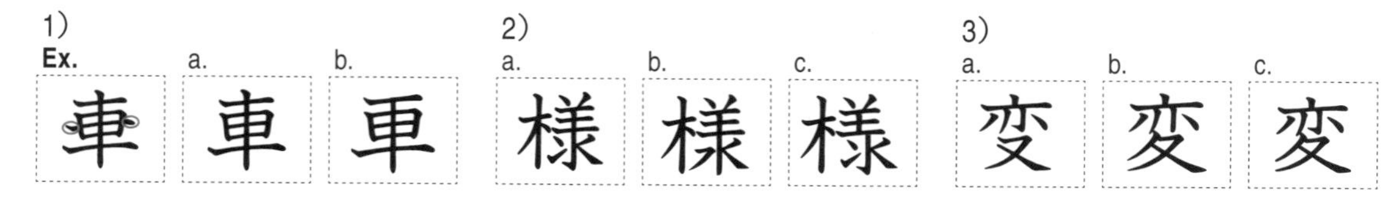

Class: __________ Name: ________________________

4 Complete kanji 1)-14) by adding an element from the boxes below.

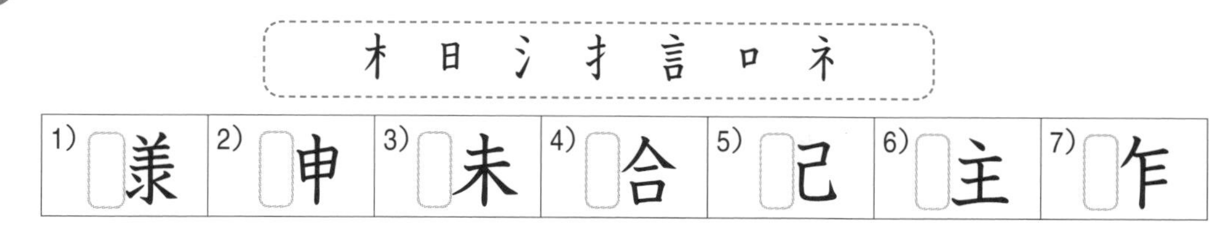

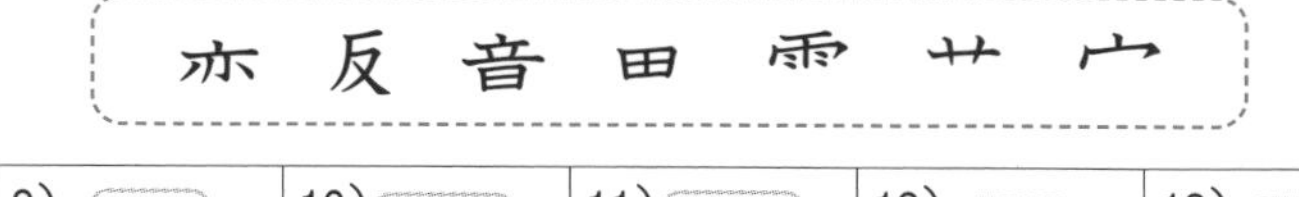

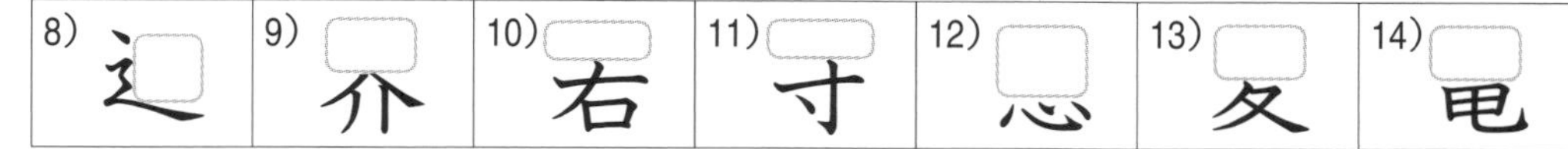

5 Circle the correct combination of kanji and its *okurigana*. Then, write its meaning in __.

1) ［a. 拾う　b. 拾ろう］ __________

2) ［a. 返す　b. 返えす］ __________

3) ［a. 守る　b. 守もる］ __________

4) ［a. 変な　b. 変んな］ __________

5) ［a. 変る　b. 変わる］ __________

6) ［a. 変る　b. 変える］ __________

7) ［a. 止る　b. 止まる］ __________

8) ［a. 止る　b. 止める］ __________

9) ［a. 若い　b. 若かい］ __________

6 You dropped your kanji flash cards again! Pick them up and organize them into nine pairs of kanji compounds. Write the kanji in the boxes, the compounds' readings in ( ), and meanings in __. You may use the same kanji twice.

Class: ＿＿＿＿＿　Name: ＿＿＿＿＿＿＿＿＿＿＿＿

7 Circle the correct kanji or kanji compound. Then, write its reading in hiragana in ＿.

Ex. 私はいつか［(a. 海外)／b. 界外］に行ってみたい。
かいがい

1)［a. 昨日／b. 作日］学校でどんな［a. 行時／b. 行事］がありましたか。

＿＿＿＿＿＿　＿＿＿＿＿＿

2)［a. 内／b. 肉］の料理を［a. 注文／b. 中文］してください。

＿＿＿＿＿＿　＿＿＿＿＿＿

3) 借(か)りたお金を［a. 返／b. 帰］さなくてはいけないから、家に［a. 返／b. 帰］って、さいふを

＿＿＿＿＿＿　＿＿＿＿＿＿

持ってこようと思う。

4)［a. 意味／b. 音味］がよく分かりません。もう一度［a. 行／b. 言］ってください。

＿＿＿＿＿＿　＿＿＿＿＿＿

5) 将来(しょうらい)、日本の［a. 社会／b. 会社］で［a. 働／b. 動］きたいから、日本の文化や

＿＿＿＿＿＿　＿＿＿＿＿＿

［a. 社会／b. 世界］について勉強している。

＿＿＿＿＿＿

8 For each picture, fill in ＿ with the corresponding kanji word or compound using kanji from this lesson. Use the dictionary form and add *okurigana* as necessary.

Ex.

借(か)りた自転車を＿返す＿。

1)

道でお金を＿＿＿＿＿＿。

2)

ルールを＿＿＿＿＿＿。

3)

雪で＿＿＿＿が＿＿＿＿。

4)

＿＿＿＿に＿＿＿＿＿＿。

5)

ネットで新聞の＿＿＿＿を読む。

6)

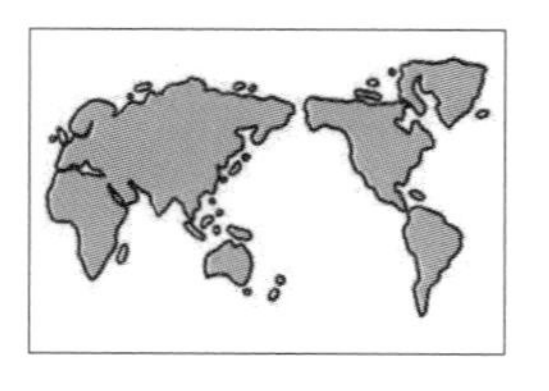

これは＿＿＿＿＿＿地図(ちず)だ。

7)

＿＿＿＿＿レンジでご飯(はん)を温(あたた)める。

8)

注文をＬサイズからＳサイズに＿＿＿＿＿＿。

Class: ____________ Name: ____________________________

9 Fill in each box to complete kanji compounds. Each word should be read in the direction that the arrow indicates. Then, provide the reading for each word in __.

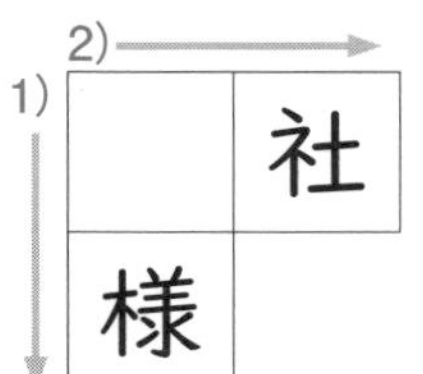

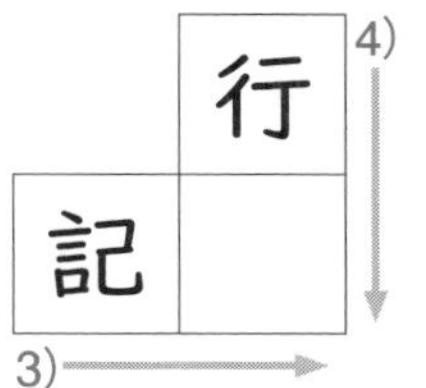

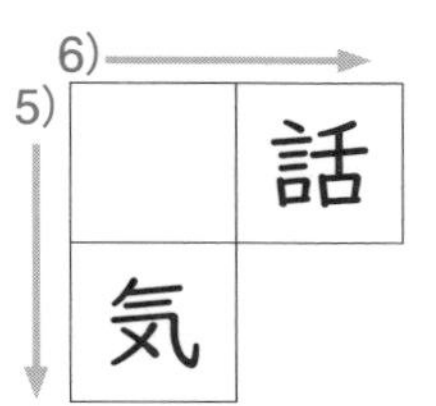

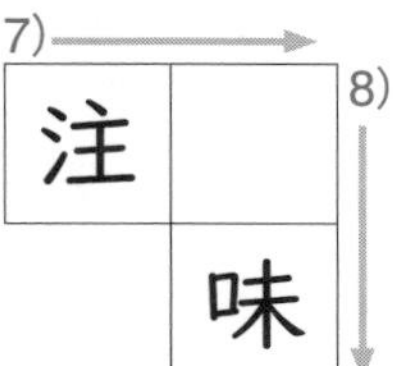

1) ____________ 3) ____________ 5) ____________ 7) ____________

2) ____________ 4) ____________ 6) ____________ 8) ____________

10 Provide the readings for words 1)-9) in (　), then match each word with its explanation on the right.

1) 一度　(　　　　　　　　)・　　　　・今日の前の日

2) 勉強中　(　　　　　　　　)・　　　　・「一回」と同じ意味

3) 世界中　(　　　　　　　　)・　　　　・今、勉強をしていること

4) 海外　(　　　　　　　　)・　　　　・初め

5) 神様　(　　　　　　　　)・　　　　・地球(ちきゅう) (earth) にある全部(ぜんぶ)の国

6) 小学校　(　　　　　　　　)・　　　　・「外国」の他(ほか)の言い方

7) 最初　(　　　　　　　　)・　　　　・例えば、天照(あまてらす) (the Japanese Sun goddess) やゼウス (Zeus)

8) 昨日　(　　　　　　　　)・　　　　・気をつけること

9) 注意　(　　　　　　　　)・　　　　・日本で6才(さい)から12才(さい)まで勉強する所

11 When the same kanji is used twice, 々 is used in place of the repeated kanji. Connect each word with its reading and meaning as in the example.

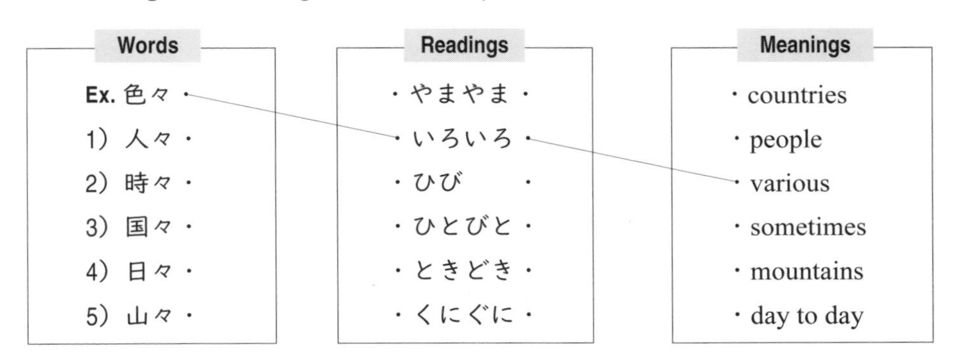

Lesson 13

Class: ___________ Name: ________________________

★★ 12 Provide the readings for the kanji of the underlined words. Note that the same kanji may have different readings depending on how it is used.

1) ネットや電話で世界中の人々と話すことができます。
a. 電話 b. 世界中 c. 人々 d. 話す

2) 勉強中に意味が分からない単語(たんご)がたくさんあったから、何度も教科書(きょうかしょ)を見た。
a. 勉強中 b. 意味 c. 何度

3) 会社で、最近(さいきん)働く所が変わって、仕事が大変になった。
a. 働く b. 所 c. 変わって d. 仕事 e. 大変

4) この神社には動物の神様がいるそうです。来週おもしろそうな行事があるから、行ってみようと思います。色々な行き方がありますが、電車と車と、どちらの方が便利(べんり)ですか。
a. 神社 b. 動物 c. 神様 d. 来週 e. 行事 f. 行って g. 色々 h. 行き方 i. 電車 j. 車 k. 方

5) A：マーカーがたくさんありますね。何色がありますか。
a. 何色

B：茶色が一本と青(あお)が二本と赤(あか)が三本あります。それから、黒(くろ)が四本ありますよ。
b. 茶色 c. 一本 d. 二本 e. 三本 f. 四本

6) 小さい子どもや小学生が電子レンジを使う時は、注意してください。
a. 小さい b. 小学生 c. 電子 d. 使う e. 注意

7) 中学生の時、初めて海外に行った。最初に飛行機(ひこうき)の中から海を見た時は、とても感動(かんどう)した。
a. 中学生 b. 初めて c. 海外 d. 最初 e. 中 f. 海

★★ 13 Provide the kanji for the underlined hiragana words. Add *okurigana* as necessary. The numbers in (　) indicate the total number of kanji that should be provided.

1) きのうは台風(たいふう)ででんしゃがとまって、たいへんだった。(7)
a. きのう b. でんしゃ c. とまって d. たいへん

2) このウェブサイトにはせかいじゅうの祭(まつ)りやぎょうじのきじがでています。(8)
a. せかいじゅう b. ぎょうじ c. きじ d. でて

3) くるまを運転(うんてん)する時は、歩(ある)いている人にちゅういして、ルールをまもって運転(うんてん)してください。(4)
a. くるま b. ちゅうい c. まもって

4) 最近(さいきん)、わかいひとたちが富士山(ふじさん)のゴミをひろうボランティアに参加(さんか)しているそうだ。(4)
a. わかい b. ひとたち c. ひろう

5) 凸はへんな漢字(かんじ)ですね。この漢字(かんじ)のいみとよみかたを教(おし)えてくださいませんか。(5)
a. へんな b. いみ c. よみかた

6) 図書館(としょかん)の本をかえすばしょがかわったから、こんど行く時はきをつけてください。
a. かえす b. ばしょ c. かわった d. こんど e. き

それから、図書館(としょかん)のまえにはくるまをとめられませんよ。(10)
f. まえ g. くるま h. とめられません

★★★ 14 Using p.120 #2 of *TOBIRA II* as a model, write about rules and manners for a place you visit often. Use kanji that you have learned in LL3-13 as much as possible.

Class: ________ Name: ________________

読む練習(れんしゅう) | Reading practice

▶『とびら II』L13 #2 (p.117) を見て、やってください。

「よさこい祭(まつ)り」の記事を読んで、質問(しつもん)に答(こた)えましょう。

Guessing the meaning of katakana words from context

1) Guess the meanings of the following katakana words and write them in __.

a. パレード ________ b. ステージ ________ c. カラフルなコスチューム ________

d. メロディ ________ e. ミックスする ________ f. スタイル ________

Identifying the 5Ws and 1H

2) The 5Ws (who, what, when, where, and why) and 1H (how) can be used to get at the important information about an event. Complete the table below by answering questions (1)-(6) based on the information in the article.

(1) いつ	(2) どこで	(3) 何がありますか。
(4) 誰(だれ)が、どんなことをしますか。		
(5) いつ、誰(だれ)が、どうして始(はじ)めましたか。		
(6) 最近(さいきん)どう変わりましたか。		
最近(さいきん)、よさこい祭(まつ)りが________________。		

Comprehension check

3) Insert the appropriate words in "______から______まで" to indicate the part of the sentence that modifies each boxed word.

l.8 b. 祭(まつ)り : ______________から______________まで

l.11 c. 意味 : ______________から______________まで

l.37 f. チーム : ______________から______________まで

4) Mark ○ if the statement is true and × if it is false.

(　　)「よさこい祭(まつ)り」に参加(さんか)する人は、日本人じゃなくてはいけない。

(　　) 記事によると、音楽の中に日本のメロディが全然(ぜんぜん)入っていなくてもいいそうだ。

(　　) 記事によると、日本の古い祭(まつ)りにはルールがたくさんあるようだ。

(　　) 記事によると、「よさこい祭(まつ)り」のおどりが見られるのは日本だけだそうだ。

5)「よさこいおどり」はどうして「よさこいダンス」(l.51) になったと思いますか。

Class: ____________ Name: ______________________

書く練習(れんしゅう) | Writing practice

▶書くシートは「とびら初級(しょきゅう)WEBサイト」にあります。

Write an article about an event

Task: Write an article about a famous or interesting festival/event that is held in your community or place of origin. Try to share some information that would make the readers want to visit the event.

1 **Pre-writing activity:** Answer the questions in the table below using simple keywords or phrases in Japanese. (Do not write full sentences.) Use the "hamburger method" shown in the left-most column as a guide for organizing your article.

Opening	1)イベントの名前は何ですか。
	2)いつ、どこでありますか。
Body	3)どんなイベントですか。
	4)何がユニーク (unique) ですか。何が楽しいですか。
	5)どんなことができますか。
	6)Additional information
Closing	7)最後に言いたいこと

2 **Writing:** Based on the information above, write about a festival/event of your choice. Expand your article by adding more facts and details.

Checklist

✓	Write your article vertically from right to left and pay attention to the usage of punctuations.
✓	Use the plain forms.
✓	Organize information and your opinion logically. Use 例えば when including examples.
✓	Write at least six sentences, organized into two or more paragraphs.
✓	Use as many learned kanji as possible.
✓	Use as many grammar points as possible from the box below.

☐ V-vol と思う
☐ ～も [Emphasis]
☐ ～そうだ [Hearsay]
☐ ～ながら
☐ ～てはいけない
☐ ～なくてはいけない
☐ ～なくてもいい
☐ ～てもいい
☐ {Number／何} + Counter + も
☐ Potential forms of verbs
☐ Noun modification clauses

Exit Check

Now go back to the Kanji List for this lesson (p.26) and do the exit check to see what kanji you can read and write.

Class: ________ Name: ________________

漢字の復習(1) | Kanji Review (1) [Lessons 11-13]

11課から13課で新しく習った漢字の復習をしましょう。全部読んだり書いたりできますか。読み方や書き方が分からない漢字には○をして、よく復習しましょう。

The highlighted kanji words include new readings for kanji you've already learned.

Nouns	<もの> 着物 荷物 動画 動物 絵 時計 映画 車 電車 電子レンジ 電話 色 茶色 何色 記事 お茶 肉 牛肉 鳥肉 鳥 魚 <こと> 仕事 火事 行事 会話 <人> 自分 私達 親 人々 小学生 <所> 所 場所 神社 小学校 東京 世界 海外 <時> 昨日 九時半 <その他(other)> 例 初め 次 自由 神様 意味
Verbs	(〜を) 変える 止める 着る 集める 拾う 返す 守る 切る 楽しむ 勉強する 料理する 注文する | (〜を/について)心配する | (〜に)着く 注意する | (〜に〜を)入れる | 宝くじ(に/が)当たる | (〜で)働く | (〜が)変わる 止まる 生まれる 動く 走る | 計画を立てる 食事(を)する
Adjs.	強い 若い 茶色い 自由(な) 変(な) 大変(な) 色々(な) 同じ
Advs.	本当に 初めて 時々
Other	XよりYの方が 使い方 最初 最後 世界中 一日中 電話中 例えば 本当ですか お大事に

上の漢字をできるだけたくさん使って、「生活(everyday life)」と「旅行」の漢字マップを作ってみましょう。

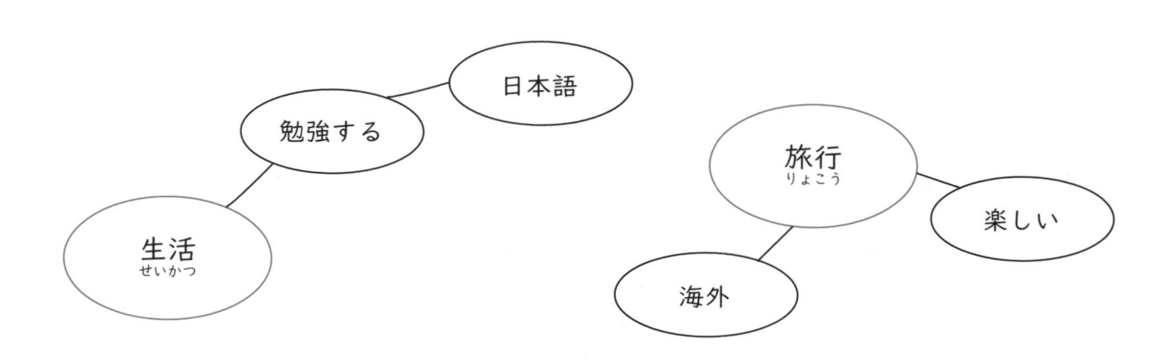

Lesson 14 大阪(おおさか)を案内(あんない)してほしいんですけど…

I'd like you to show me around Osaka...

Kanji List できるCheck ☑

	197	198	199	200	201	202	203	204	205	206	207	208	209	210	211	212	213	214	215
Kanji	開	閉	消	汚	乗	遅	困	運	転	痛	医	者	薬	服	店	部	屋	教	室
Entry Check																			
Exit Check																			

Kanji in images

Kanji in daily life Which kanji can you recognize?

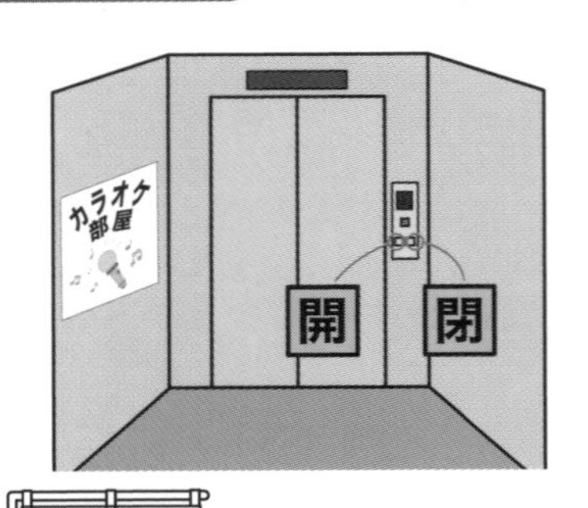

Class: ____________ Name: ______________________

漢字の練習（かんじ れんしゅう） | Kanji practice

1 Trace the gray kanji first, then write each kanji twice as neatly as possible.

S=stop F=flick R=release C=curved line ↓ → =direction ◯=note ◌=space

197	198	199	200	201	202
開 (S R C S F)	閉 (S F F)	消 (S F)	汚 (short, long, one stroke, F)	乗 (short, long, short, R S R)	遅 (R R)
開	閉	消	汚	乗	遅

203	204	205	206	207	208
困 (R S R)	運 (S R)	転 (short, long, one stroke)	痛 (R S F)	医 (R R R, one stroke)	者 (start here, R)
困	運	転	痛	医	者

Lesson 14

Class: ___________ Name: ______________________

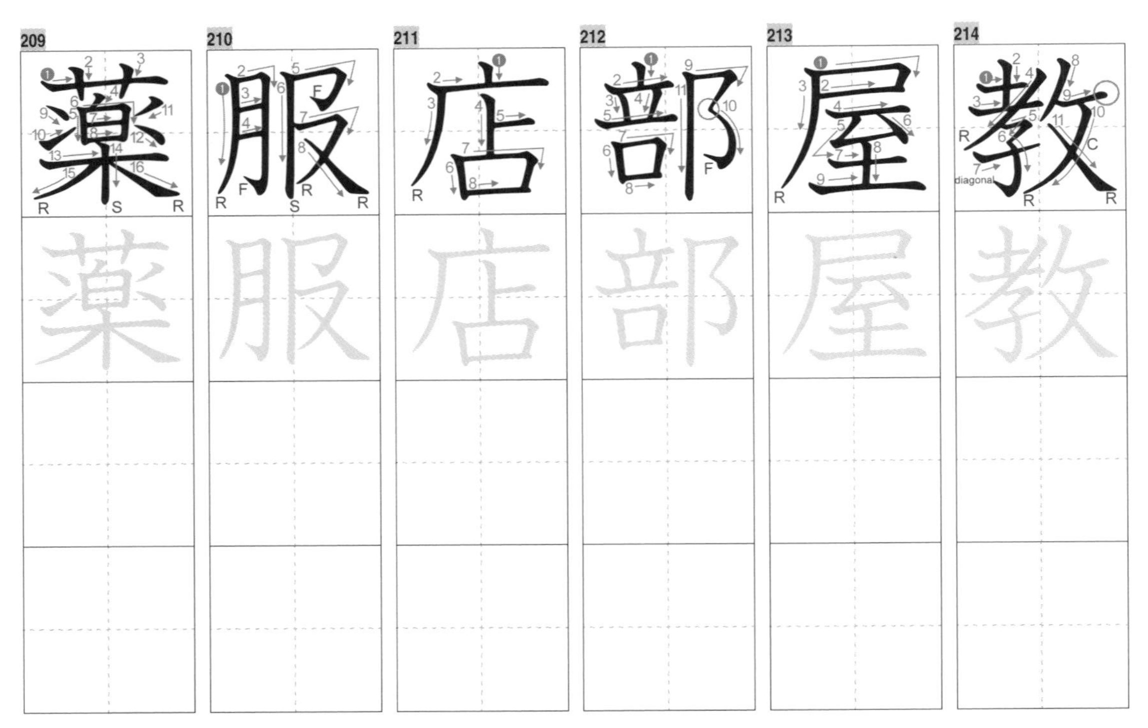

215
室

2 For each pair of kanji, circle the element or part that they have in common. Then, write the reading of the given word.

Ex. 開ける	閉める	1) 海	消す
(　　　)ける	(　　　)める	(　　　)	(　　　)す
2) 病気	痛い	3) 店	広い
(　　　)き	(　　　)い	(　　　)	(　　　)い
4) 運ぶ	遅れる	5) 薬	若い
(　　　)ぶ	(　　　)れる	(　　　)	(　　　)い
6) 運転		7) 本屋	教室
(　　　　　)		ほん(　　　)	きょう(　　　)

Class: __________ Name: ______________________

3 Fill in each __ with the verb or noun that represents the picture. Use kanji where applicable and add *okurigana* as necessary.

Ex. ＿教室＿で＿教える＿　　1) ______________　　2) ______________

3) ______________　　4) ______________　　5) ______を______

6) ______________に______　　7) ______________

4 Provide the readings for the kanji words in __. Then, categorize their corresponding letters into the given groups as in the example.

Ex. 開く ＿あく＿	a. 開ける ______	b. 閉まる ______
c. 閉める ______	d. 消す ______	e. 消える ______
f. 汚い ______	g. 汚れる ______	h. 汚す ______
i. 遅れる ______	j. 遅い ______	k. 困る ______
l. 痛い ______	m. 教える ______	n. 転ぶ ______
o. 運ぶ ______		

Intransitive verbs	Transitive verbs	Adjectives
Ex.		

Lesson 14

Class: ________ Name: ________________

5 For each picture, fill in __ with the corresponding word using kanji from this lesson. Add *okurigana* as necessary.

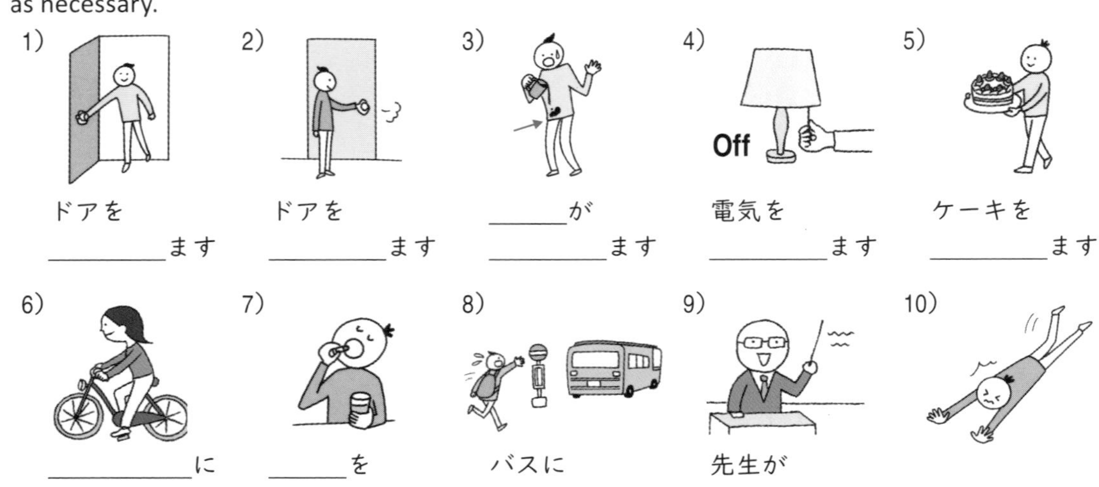

1) ドアを ________ます
2) ドアを ________ます
3) ______が ________ます
4) 電気を ________ます
5) ケーキを ________ます
6) ________に ________ます
7) ______を 飲みます
8) バスに ________ます
9) 先生が ________ます
10) ________ます

6 Provide the readings for words 1)-9) in ( ), then match each word with its explanation on the right.

1) 消しゴム	( ) ・	・	病気の時に飲む物
2) 医者	( ) ・	・	えんぴつで書いた字を消す物
3) 部屋	( ) ・	・	着る物（例：Tシャツ）
4) 教会	( ) ・	・	寝たり勉強したりする所
5) 薬	( ) ・	・	同じ宗教の人が会う所
6) 花屋	( ) ・	・	病気をチェックする人
7) 服	( ) ・	・	物を売っている所
8) 教室	( ) ・	・	授業を受ける所
9) 店	( ) ・	・	花を売っている店

7 Write the kanji that corresponds to the given meaning. Then, provide the reading and meaning of each compound word as in the example.

Ex.
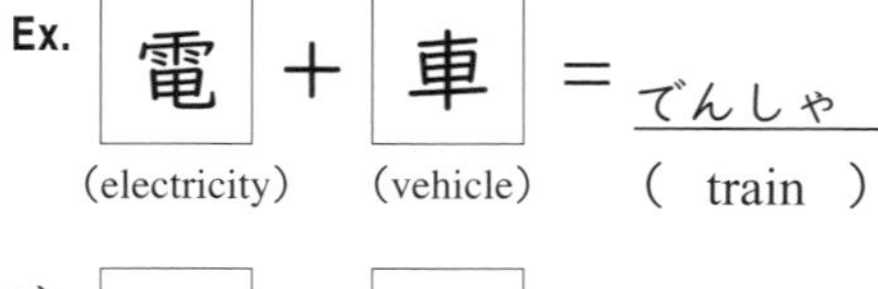

電 (electricity) + 車 (vehicle) = でんしゃ (train)

1)
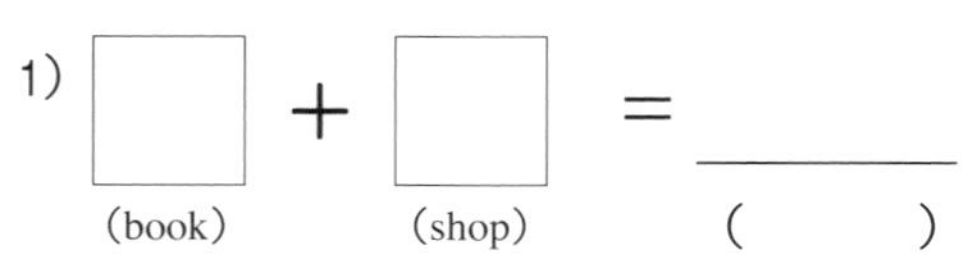

☐ (book) + ☐ (shop) = ________ ( )

2)
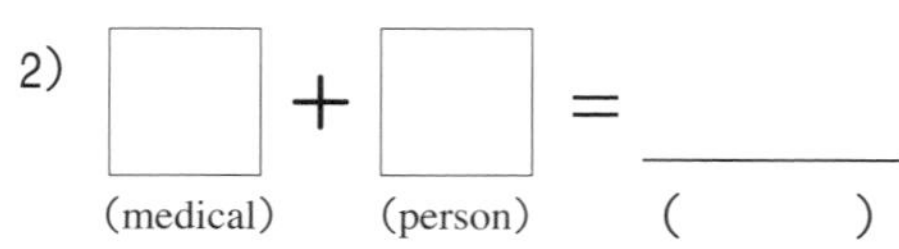

☐ (medical) + ☐ (person) = ________ ( )

3)
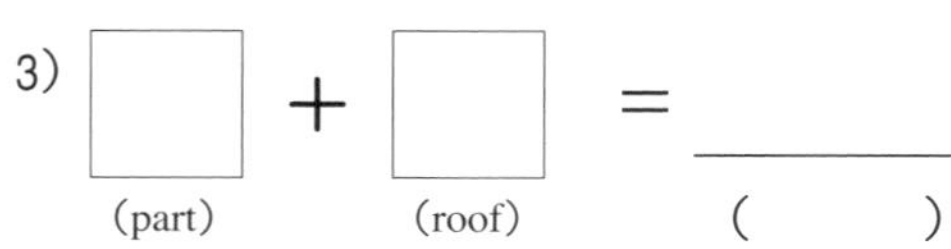

☐ (part) + ☐ (roof) = ________ ( )

4) ☐ (to teach) + ☐ (room) = ________ ( )

5) ☐ (to transport) + ☐ (to rotate) = ________ ( )

Class: ___________ Name: ___________________________

8 Provide the readings for the kanji of the underlined words. Note that the same kanji may have different readings depending on how it is used.

1) 教室にはこの入口から入ってください。
  a. 入口　b. 入って

2) A：キッチンが汚いですね。　B：すみません。料理した時、汚してしまいました。
  a. 汚い　b. 汚して

3) 引(ひ)っ越(こ)しするんですか。ソファを運ぶ車は私が運転しますよ。
  a. 運ぶ　b. 運転

4) 自転車に乗っている時、転んでしまいました。
  a. 自転車　b. 転んで

5) テニス部の部屋はどこですか。
  a. 部　b. 部屋

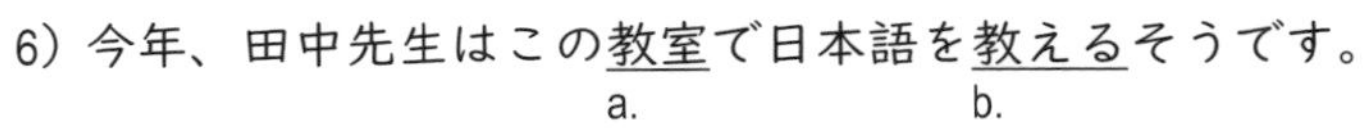

6) 今年、田中先生はこの教室で日本語を教えるそうです。
  a. 教室　b. 教える

7)「最悪」は「一番悪い」という意味です。
  a. 最悪　b. 悪い

8) せきが出るんです。すみませんが、あの箱(はこ) (box) から薬を出してくれませんか。
  a. 出る　b. 出して

9) 日本には色々な妖怪(ようかい)やお化けの話があります。おもしろい文化だと思います。
  a. お化け　b. 文化

10) 火曜日にバーベキューをしたいんですが、とびら公園(こうえん)では火が使えますか。
  a. 火曜日　b. 火

9 Provide the readings for the given words in 1)-5), then write a sentence that uses them.

Ex. 開ける（ あける ）　閉める（ しめる ）
➡ ドアを開けたら、閉めておいてください。

1) 部屋（　　　　）　汚い（　　　　）
➡ ______________________________

2) 痛い（　　　　）　薬（　　　　）　二日よい（　　　　）
➡ ______________________________

3) 開く（　　　　）　出口（　　　　）
➡ ______________________________

4) 乗り遅れる（　　　　）　困る（　　　　）
➡ ______________________________

5) 入口（　　　　）　電気（　　　　）　消える（　　　　）
➡ ______________________________

Lesson 14

Class: __________ Name: ____________________

10 Provide the kanji for the underlined hiragana words. Add *okurigana* as necessary. The numbers in ( ) indicate the total number of kanji that should be provided.

私の大学

1) 私の大学を紹介(しょうかい)します。私の大学は大きいです。新しくてきれいなジムがあって、学生はここでうんどう[a.]できます。きれいなきょうかい[b.]もあります。それから、キャンパスには小さい病院(びょういん)があって、頭(あたま)がいたい[c.]時、いしゃ[d.]にくすり[e.]をもらうことができます。大学の近(ちか)くにはいろいろ[f.]なカフェやみせ[g.]があります。私はよくふく[h.]を見に行ったり、ほんや[i.]に行ったりします。(14)

2) 駅(えき)の1番でぐち[a.]から大学まで歩(ある)いて5分ぐらいでとても便利(べんり)ですから、学生はたいていでんしゃ[b.]を使いますが、私は毎日、じてんしゃ[c.]で大学に行きます。でも、雨の日はバスで行きます。雨の日はバスがおくれる[d.]から、きょうしつ[e.]に行くのがおそく[f.]なります。だから、いつもこまります[g.]。(12)

3) 私は今、寮(りょう)に住んでいます。大学に入る時、父と一緒(いっしょ)に家から車をうんてん[a.]して、荷物をはこび[b.]ました。寮(りょう)のいりぐち[c.]のドアはじどう[d.]でしまり[e.]ます。知らない人がドアをあける[f.]ことはできません。それから、夜(よる)おそい[g.]時間にでんき[h.]がきえて[i.]いる時は、人が来たら、じどうででんきがつきますから、安全(あんぜん)です。(13)

4) 私の大学は楽しい所がたくさんあるから、今、いいおもいで[a.]をたくさん作っています。みなさんの大学のこともおしえて[b.]ください。(3)

11 Using #10 as a model, write about the facilities, transportation services, and stores around your school's campus. Use kanji that you have learned in LL3-14 as much as possible.

Class: __________ Name: ____________________

読む練習 | Reading practice

▶『とびらII』L14 #2(p.157)を見て、やってください。

アイがクラスメートとお化けやしき (haunted house) に行った時の会話を読んで、質問に答えましょう。

Visualizing

1) Based on the conversation among Ai and her classmates, complete the picture of the haunted house below with items a.-f. in the box. You may draw each item, or simply write the letter for each into the appropriate place in the picture.

a. ろうそく　b. 人形　c. テレビ　d. お化け　e. かぎ　f. たこ焼きのチケット

Understanding Japanese sentence structure: Transitive and intransitive verbs

2) **Step 1** Mark the underlined verb as either T (a transitive verb) or I (an intransitive verb) in ( ).

Step 2 Draw a box around the subject of each intransitive verb and the direct object of each transitive verb, then circle the accompanying particle. If the subject or direct object is omitted, insert it and its accompanying particle into the sentence.

l.9	火が<u>ついてる</u>	(　)	l.15	人形が<u>落ちてる</u>	(　)
l.16	血が<u>出てるよ</u>	(　)	l.20	ドアを<u>開けなくちゃ</u>	(　)
l.21	ドアが<u>閉まってる</u>	(　)	l.21	かぎも<u>かかってる</u>	(　)
l.21	<u>開かない</u>	(　)	l.22	<u>開けて</u>みたら	(　)
l.23	<u>開いた</u>	(　)	l.26	チケットを<u>落とした</u>	(　)
l.28	<u>入れてあった</u>	(　)			

*See Conversation Tips on p.15 *TOBIRA II* for contracted forms.

Comprehension check

3) Mark ○ if the statement is true and × if it is false.

ぼくがリーマンだよ

(　) デヴィもエンマもアイも、お化けやしきに入りたかった。

(　) エンマはチケットを落としてしまったから、たこ焼きが食べられないようだ。

(　) デヴィは顔出しパネルでとった写真をSNSにアップするようだ。

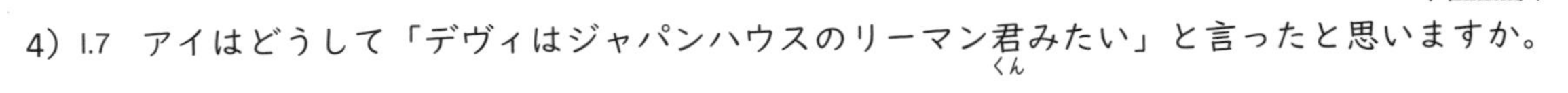

4) l.7 アイはどうして「デヴィはジャパンハウスのリーマン君みたい」と言ったと思いますか。

Lesson 14

Class: ________ Name: ______________

書く練習(れんしゅう) | Writing practice

▶書くシートは「とびら初級(しょきゅう)WEBサイト」にあります。

Create your own お化けやしき(haunted house)

Task：おもしろくてこわいお化けやしきを自分で考(かんが)えて、それについて説明(せつめい)を書きましょう。

1 Pre-writing activity: Write your ideas for a haunted house using simple keywords or phrases in Japanese.

①あなたがこわいもの／大きらいなもの／見たくないもの etc. ②お化けやしきのテーマ (theme)	③そのお化けやしきには、どんなお化けがいますか。何がありますか。

④あなたの考(かんが)えたお化けやしきについて お化けやしきの名前： 場所： チケットのねだん：	お化けやしきの絵：

2 Writing: Based on your outline above, describe your own haunted house in detail.

Checklist

✓	Use the です・ます forms.
✓	Clearly describe your creative ideas for your own お化けやしき in detail.
✓	Write at least six sentences, organized into two or more paragraphs.
✓	Use as many learned kanji as possible.
✓	Use as many grammar points as possible from the box below.

☐ V-transitive ☐ V-intransitive ☐ V-intransitive＋ている [A state of something/someone]
☐ V-transitive＋てある [State resulting in from purposeful action] ☐～てしまう ☐～かもしれない
☐～すぎる ☐～し、～し ☐～てほしい ☐～たら ☐ Noun modification clauses

Exit Check

Now go back to the Kanji List for this lesson (p.36) and do the exit check to see what kanji you can read and write.

COLUMN 2

日本語の歌を歌ってみよう

日本の小学校の教科書にもある有名な歌を二つ紹介します。日本語で歌ってみましょう。

翼をください

作詞 (lyrics)：山上路夫　作曲 (music)：村井邦彦

今私の願いごとが　かなうならば　翼がほしい
この背中に　鳥のように　白い翼　つけてください
この大空に　翼を広げ　飛んで行きたいよ
悲しみのない　自由な空へ　翼はためかせ　行きたい

今富とか名誉ならば　いらないけど　翼がほしい
子どもの時　夢見たこと　今も同じ　夢に見ている
この大空に　翼を広げ　飛んで行きたいよ
悲しみのない　自由な空へ　翼はためかせ　行きたい

翼：wings　私の願いごとが かなうならば：if my wish came true　つける：to put (on)
背中：back [body part]　広げ(る)：to spread　悲しみのない：no sadness
はためかせ(る)：to flap　富：wealth　名誉：honor

さんぽ

※アニメ映画『となりのトトロ』の歌

作詞 (lyrics)：中川李枝子　作曲 (music)：久石譲

Match the pictures below with the shaded words in the lyrics.

歩こう歩こう　私は元気　歩くの大好き　どんどん行こう
坂道　トンネル　草っぱら　一本橋に　でこぼこじゃり道
クモの巣くぐって　下り道

歩こう歩こう　私は元気　歩くの大好き　どんどん行こう
ミツバチぶんぶん花畑　ひなたにトカゲ　ヘビは昼寝
バッタが飛んで　まがり道

歩こう歩こう　私は元気　歩くの大好き　どんどん行こう
キツネもタヌキも　出ておいで　探検しよう　林の奥まで
友達たくさん　うれしいな　友達たくさん　うれしいな

どんどん：further and futher　坂道：slope　草っぱら：meadow　一本橋：log bridge
でこぼこじゃり道：bumpy gravel road　くぐる：to pass through　下り道：way down
ぶんぶん：[buzzing sound]　花畑：field of flowers　ひなた：sunny spot
まがり道：winding road　出ておいで：Come out!　探検：exploration
林の奥：deep in the forest　(うれしい)な：[exclamation particle]

Lesson 15 ちょっと分かりにくいと思うんですけど…

I think it might be a little difficult to understand...

Kanji List できるCheck ☑

	216	217	218	219	220	221	222	223	224	225	226	227	228	229	230	231	232	233	234 (E9)
Kanji	続	助	調	忘	図	館	質	問	宿	題	試	験	受	練	習	飯	族	夕	馬
Entry Check																			
Exit Check																			

Kanji meanings in images

Hashtags Which kanji can you recognize?

#自習室 #宿題
#勉強 #試験 #夏休み

#献血ルーム #助けよう

#うさぎ #ネザーランドドワーフ
#ご飯 #家族

#大使館 #通訳
#英語コーチング

#練習 #コツコツ #続ける

#新潟(にいがた) #名物料理
#へぎそば #調べてみた

#桜 #心のきよらかさ
#私を忘れないで #花言葉

#食べ物スタンプ #質問
#問題 #分かる人

Class: __________ Name: ____________________

漢字の練習 | Kanji practice

1 Trace the gray kanji first, then write each kanji twice as neatly as possible.

S=stop F=flick R=release C=curved line ↓→=direction ◯=note ◌=space

216	217	218	219	220	221
続	助	調	忘	図	館
続	助	調	忘	図	館

222	223	224	225	226	227
質	問	宿	題	試	験
質	問	宿	題	試	験

Class: __________ Name: ______________________

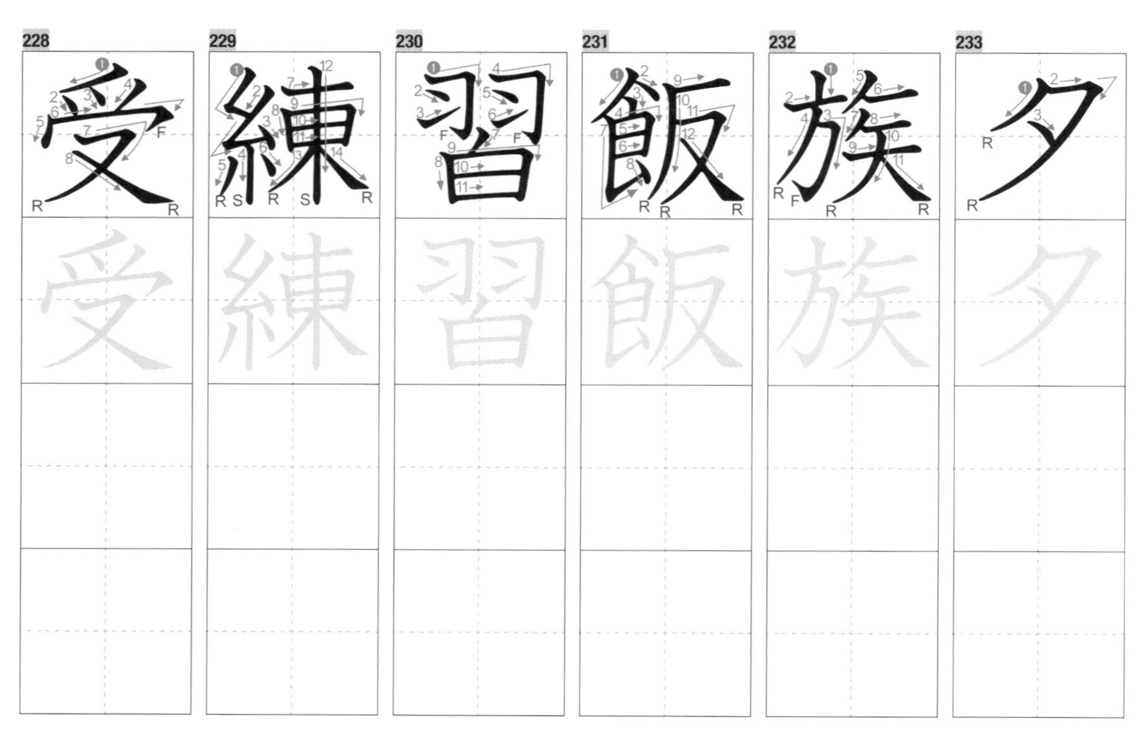

234

馬

馬

2 Make kanji by combining the elements provided, then write their readings in (   ) as in the example.

Ex.1 且＋力＝助ける（たすける）

Ex.2（言＋式）＋（馬＋㑒）＝試験（しけん）

1）糸＋売＝□ける（　　　　）

2）言＋周＝□べる（　　　　）

3）羽＋白＝□う（　　　　）

4）⺤＋冖＋又＝□ける（　　　　）

5）（斦＋貝）＋（門＋口）＝□□（　　　　）

6）（宀＋豕）＋（方＋𠂉＋矢）＝□□（　　　　）

Class: __________ Name: ____________________

3 Circle the mistake(s) in each kanji, then write the correct one in the box.

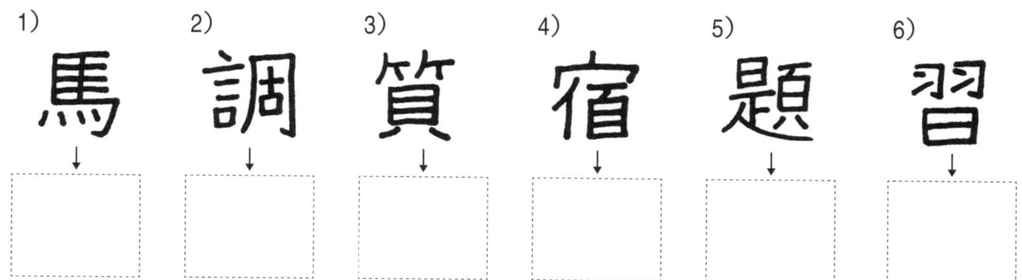

4 Fill in __ with the appropriate *okurigana* as in the example. Pay attention to the particles that precede the verbs.

Ex. いい医者を見<u>　つけ　</u>ます。

1) 日本語の勉強を続________ます。　　2) 困っている人を助________ます。

3) 車の運転を習________ます。　　4) いい店を調________ます。

5) 時々宿題を忘________ます。　　6) 試験を受________ます。

7) 朝(あさ)、体を動________ます。　　8) お金が足________ないから、これは買えません。

Lesson 15

5 For each incomplete kanji, write in the missing element. Then, provide the reading for the underlined part in (　).

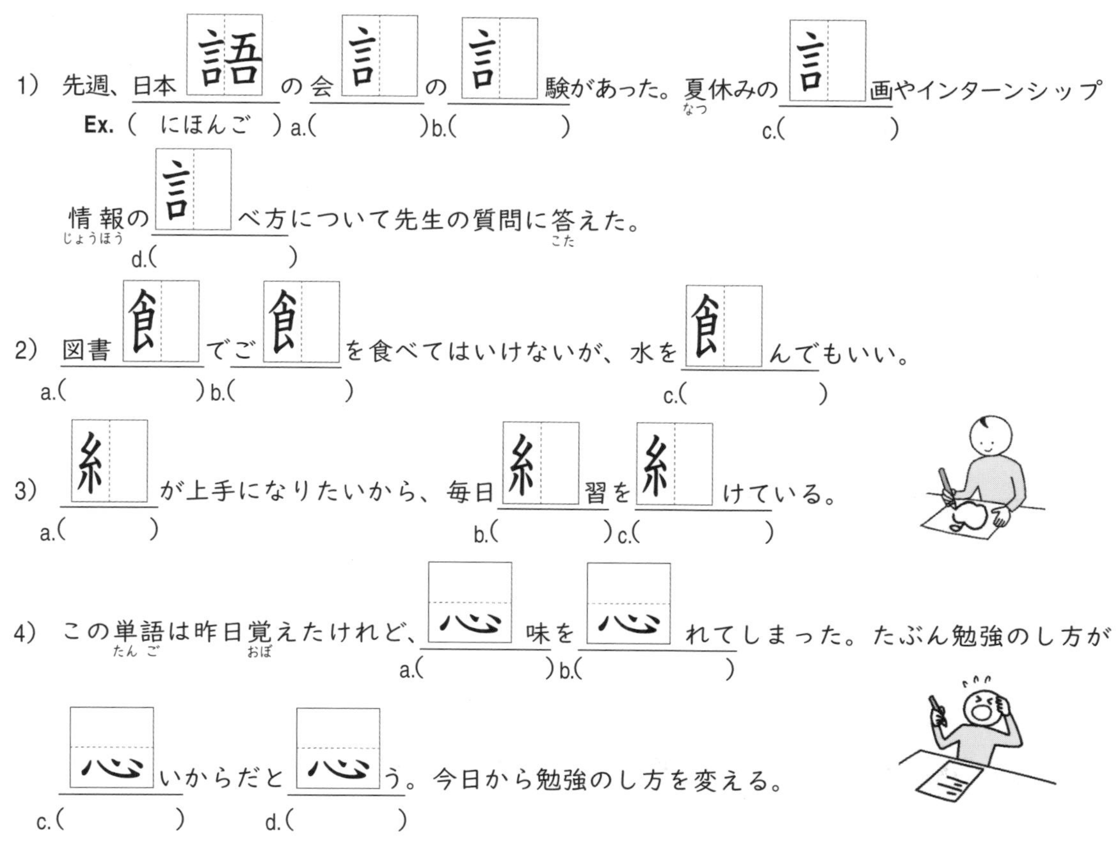

6 Organize the kanji flash cards into six pairs of kanji compounds. Write the kanji in the boxes and their readings in (   ). Note that two cards are used twice.

7 For each picture, fill in __ with the corresponding word using kanji from this lesson. Add *okurigana* as necessary.

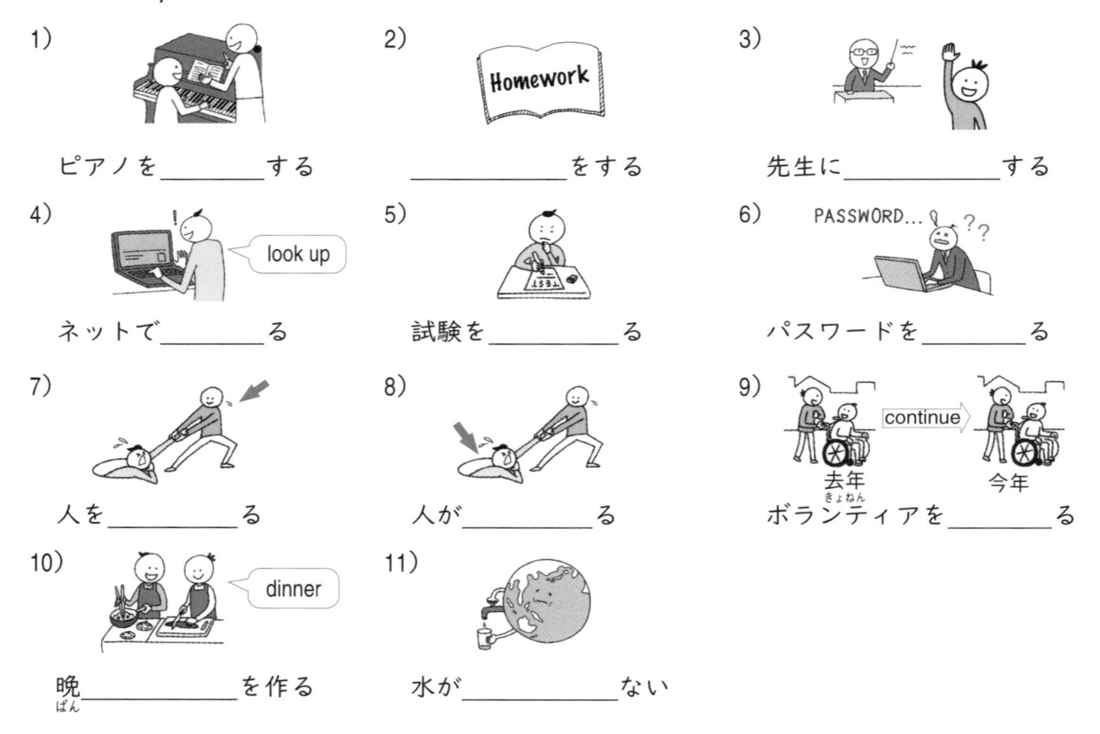

8 Provide the readings for the following words. Each word should be read in the direction that the arrow indicates.

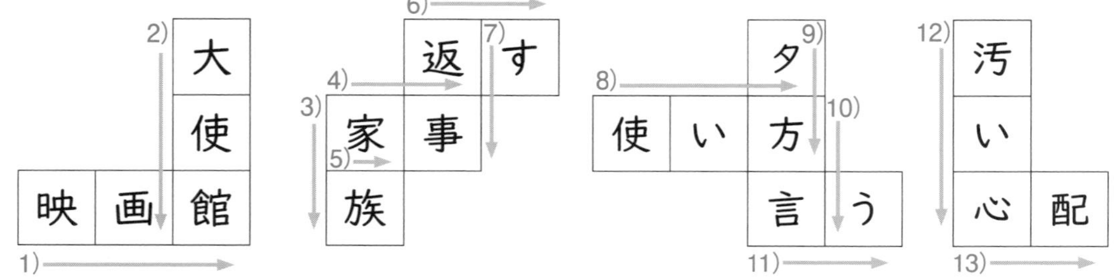

Class: ____________ Name: ____________________

14)↓ 15)→ 16)↓

質	宿
問	題

17)↓ 18)→

練	
習	う

19)↓ 20)→

世	
話	す

1) ________ 2) ________ 3) ________ 4) ________

5) ________ 6) ________ 7) ________ 8) ________

9) ________ 10) ________ 11) ________ 12) ________

13) ________ 14) ________ 15) ________ 16) ________

17) ________ 18) ________ 19) ________ 20) ________

★★ 9 Provide the readings for the following kanji words and compounds in __. Then, fill in ( ) with the corresponding letter of the most appropriate word to complete each sentence.

1) a. 足りなかった ________ b. 忘れた ________ c. ご飯 ________

昼(ひる)（　）を買おうと思ったけれど、お金が（　）。カードも（　）。だから、家に帰った。

2) a. 意見 ________ b. 体 ________ c. 勉強 ________

（　）にいいことについて医者の（　）を聞いて、とても（　）になった。

3) a. 家族 ________ b. 返事 ________ c. 夕方 ________

土曜日の（　）まで（　）と旅行(りょこう)中だから、メールの（　）が少(すこ)し遅くなるかもしれません。

4) a. 家事 ________ b. 世話 ________ c. せんたく物 ________

私は子どもの時、みんなの（　）をたたんだり、弟たちの（　）をしたりしました。よく（　）を手伝(てつだ)う子どもでした。

5) a. 着がえて ________ b. 海 ________ c. 水着 ________

家から（　）まですぐに行けるから、ここで服から（　）に（　）ください。

6) a. 動かない ________ b. 助けよう ________ c. 見つけた ________

山で（　）小さいフクロウ (owl) を（　）。（　）と思って近(ちか)くに行ったら、キノコ (mushroom) だった。

Lesson 15

Class: ___________ Name: ___________________________

10 Provide the kanji for the underlined hiragana words. Add *okurigana* and other hiragana as necessary. The numbers in ( ) indicate the total number of kanji that should be provided.

1) 今日は午前中にかじをして、ペットのどうぶつたちのせわをした後で、せんたくものをたたんだ。(8)
a. かじ b. どうぶつたち c. せわ d. もの

2) 午後はごはんを食べてから、メールにへんじをした。それから、ピアノのれんしゅうを始め(はじ)て、ゆうがたまでつづけた。(8)
a. ごはん b. へんじ c. れんしゅう d. ゆうがた e. つづけた

3) 大学生のこころのもんだいについて授業(じゅぎょう)でいけんを言わなくてはいけないから、としょかんに行って少(すこ)ししらべた。その後で、ジムではしって体をうごかした。(11)
a. こころ b. もんだい c. いけん d. としょかん e. しらべた f. はしって g. うごかした

4) 12月にJLPTという日本語のしけんをうけるから、今色々なれんしゅうをやっている。ならった漢字(かんじ)をわすれてしまったから、漢字(かんじ)のしゅくだいも復習(ふくしゅう)している。(7)
a. しけん b. うける c. ならった d. わすれて e. しゅくだい

5) バイトをしていて勉強する時間がたりないから、奨学金(しょうがくきん)をもらえたらたすかる。もっと大学にお金がない学生をたすけてほしい。(3)
a. たりない b. たすかる c. たすけて

11 Provide the readings for the kanji of the underlined words.

私の日本語の勉強のし方

まず、授業(じゅぎょう)でたくさん話す練習をします。次に、宿題をやって分からない問題があったら、先生に質問します。単語(たんご)や漢字(かんじ)はすぐ忘れてしまうから、何回もアプリを使って覚(おぼ)えます。それから、友達に教えてもらったり自分で調べたりして、何でもいいから、毎日日本語の動画を一つ見ます。動画は若い人が使う話し方や方言が分かるから、おもしろいです。最後に、習ったことを使って書いたり話したりしてみます。ポイントは、楽しみながら勉強を続けることです。

a. 練習 b. 次に c. 宿題 d. 問題 e. 質問 f. 忘れて g. 何回も h. 使って i. 友達 j. 教えて k. 調べた l. 何でも m. 毎日 n. 動画 o. 一つ p. 若い q. 話し方 r. 方言 s. 最後に t. 習った u. 楽しみ v. 続ける

12 Using #11 as a model, write about how you study Japanese. Use kanji that you have learned in LL3-15 as much as possible.

Class: ________ Name: ________________

読む練習 | Reading practice

▶『とびら II』L15 #2(p.195) を見て、やってください。

悩み相談 (requests for advice) を読んで、質問に答えましょう。

Understanding Japanese sentence structure: Nominalizers (の and こと)

1) Insert the appropriate words in "_______から_______まで" to indicate the part of the sentence that modifies each boxed word.

Case A

l.2 **Ex.** の : インターネット から 見る まで

l.5 a. こと : ____________ から ____________ まで

Case B

l.12 b. の : ____________ から ____________ まで

l.14 c. の : ____________ から ____________ まで

l.15 d. こと : ____________ から ____________ まで

l.19 e. の : ____________ から ____________ まで

Grasping the relationship between clauses

2) The underlined parts in the requests for advice show connective expressions that indicate the relationship between clauses. Insert the most appropriate letter from the box below in ( ) to identify the function of the underlined part.

S = Sequential relationship	**O** = Opposing ideas	**M** = Manner-action relationship
R = Causal relationship [reason/cause]	**C** = Conditional relationship	**E** = Example listing

Case A

l.3 **Ex1.** ６時間ぐらい続け<u>て</u> (M)　　l.7 **Ex2.** 目が痛くなる<u>し</u> (E)

l.3 少し時間があっ<u>たら</u> ( )　　l.5 勉強しなくてはいけない<u>から</u> ( )

l.6 長い時間ネットを見てしまう<u>から</u> ( )　　l.7 成績も悪くなる<u>し</u> ( )

l.8 何でも信じてしまう<u>し</u> ( )　　l.9 かくしたりしてみました<u>が</u> ( )

Case B

l.13 友達がたくさんい<u>たら</u> ( )　　l.14 友達がいない<u>から</u> ( )

l.14 楽しそうにしているのを見<u>て</u> ( )　　l.16 誰にも連絡しない<u>から</u> ( )

l.17 ～と言います<u>が</u> ( )　　l.17 自分からさそってみ<u>て</u> ( )

l.18 いい返事がもらえなかっ<u>たら</u> ( )　　l.18 落ち込む<u>し</u> ( )

l.18 話しにくい<u>し</u> ( )　　l.19 きらいじゃありません<u>が</u> ( )

Class: ___________ Name: ________________________

Summarizing

3) List the main points of each 悩(なや)み相談(そうだん) in your own words as shown in the example. Use the plain form endings.

■ Case A：はっちさんの相談(そうだん)

Main problem	
Specific problems	・宿題や試験の勉強や、やらなくてはいけないことをする時間がない。 ・ ・ ・
Unsuccessful solutions	・ ・

■ Case B：ドレミさんの相談(そうだん)

Main problem	
Specific problems	・[　　　　　　　　　　]、うらやましくなる。 ・[　　　　　　　　　　]、はずかしいと思う。
Unsuccessful solutions (advice from her sister)	・ ・

Comprehension check

4) Mark ○ if the statement is true and × if it is false.

(　　) はっちさんはネットでよくゲームをしたり動画を見たりしているみたいだ。

(　　) はっちさんはネットの情報(じょうほう)を信(しん)じやすい人のようだ。

(　　) ドレミさんは友達が多(おお)い人がうらやましいと思っているようだ。

(　　) ドレミさんは一人でいるのはさびしいから好きじゃない。

(　　) ドレミさんは話しやすい友達をほしがっている。

5) What advice would you give? Choose one person and give your advice using the template provided below.

私は{はっちさん／ドレミさん}に「________________________________」と言います。

____からです。

Class: ＿＿＿＿＿ Name: ＿＿＿＿＿＿＿＿＿＿

書く練習 | Writing practice

▶書くシートは「とびら初級(しょきゅう)WEBサイト」にあります。

Seek advice on worries/concerns

Task： Referring to Cases A and B on p.195 of *TOBIRA II*, write your own 悩(なや)み相談(そうだん).

1 **Pre-writing activity:** Brainstorm your worries or concerns, then create an outline for your 悩(なや)み相談(そうだん) using simple keywords or phrases in Japanese.

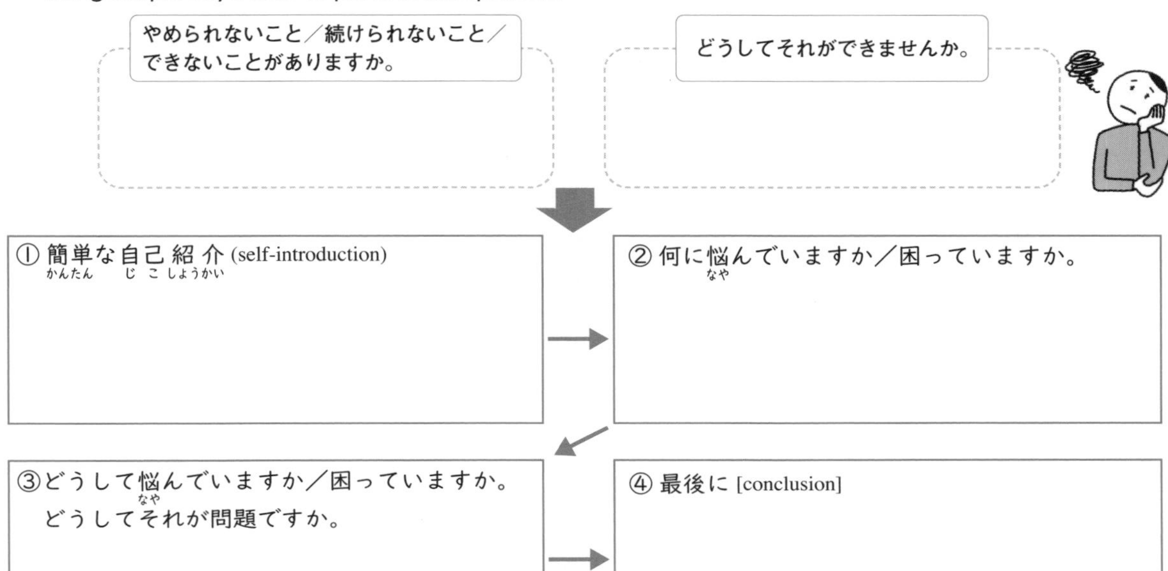

2 **Writing:** Based on the outline above, explain your worries or concerns in detail.

Checklist

✓	Use the です・ます forms.
✓	Organize your thoughts logically and write a minimum of six sentences.
✓	Use as many learned kanji as possible.
✓	Use as many grammar points as possible from the box below.

- □ ～ないで
- □ ～やすい／にくい
- □ {～た／ない}方がいい
- □ ～て{くれる／もらう}
- □ ～し～し
- □ ～たり～たりする
- □ ～てしまう

Exit Check

Now go back to the Kanji List for this lesson (p.46) and do the exit check to see what kanji you can read and write.

Lesson 16 一日しか会えなくて残念(ざんねん)です…

It's too bad we can only meet up for one day...

Kanji List できるCheck ☑

	235	236	237	238	239	240	241	242	243	244	245	246	247	248	249	250	251	252	253 (E10)
Kanji	取	泣	笑	起	始	終	決	歌	洗	台	旅	駅	朝	昼	晩	夜	漢	字	竹
Entry Check																			
Exit Check																			

Kanji in images

Kanji in daily life

Which kanji can you recognize?

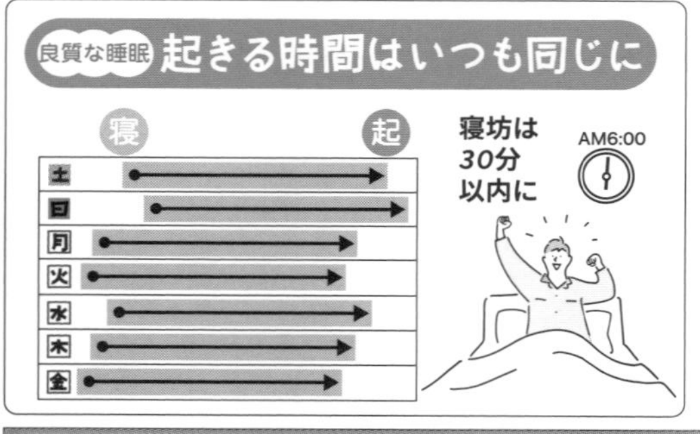

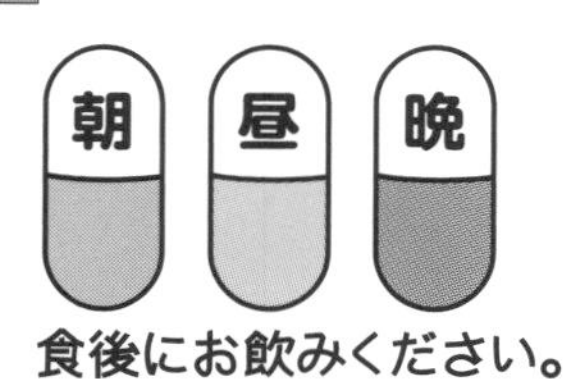

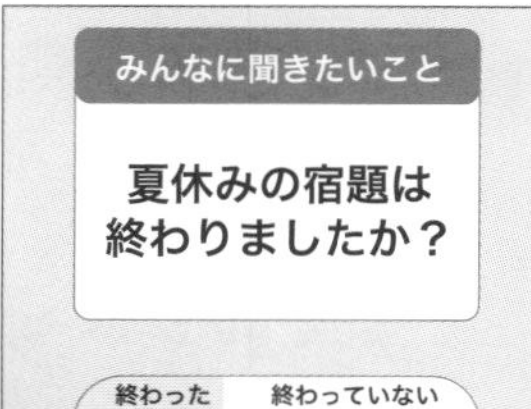

Class: ____________ Name: ______________________________

漢字の練習 | Kanji practice

1 Trace the gray kanji first, then write each kanji twice as neatly as possible.

S=stop F=flick R=release C=curved line ↓ → =direction ◯=note ◌=space

Lesson 16

Class: ___________ Name: ___________________________

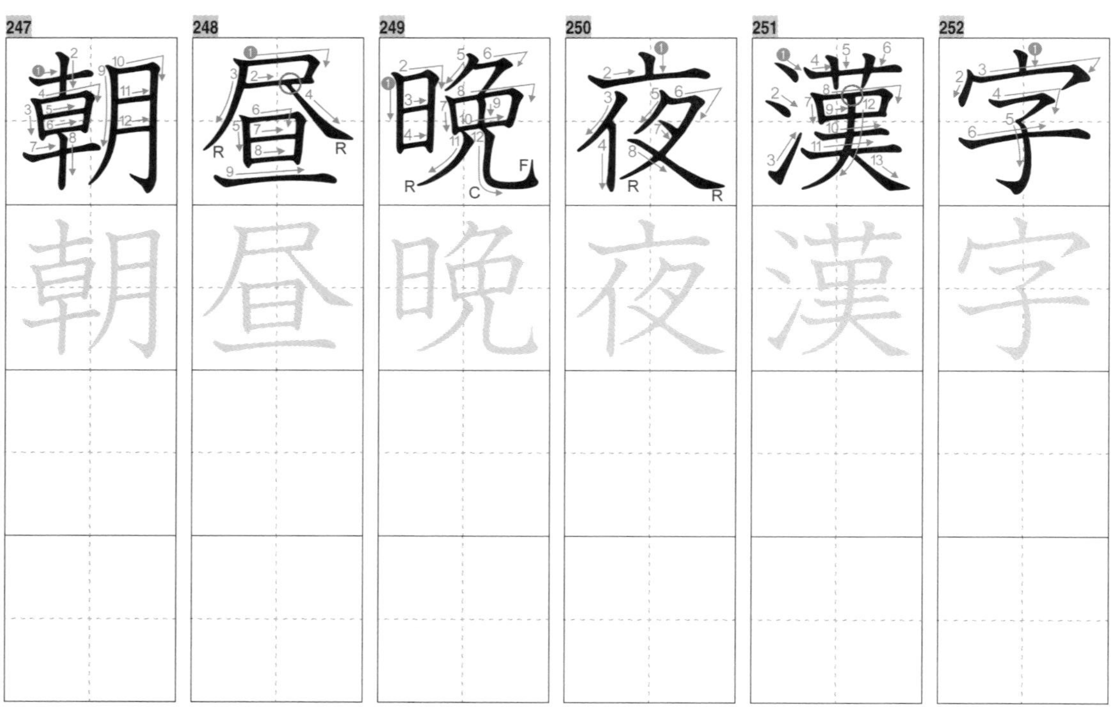

253 竹

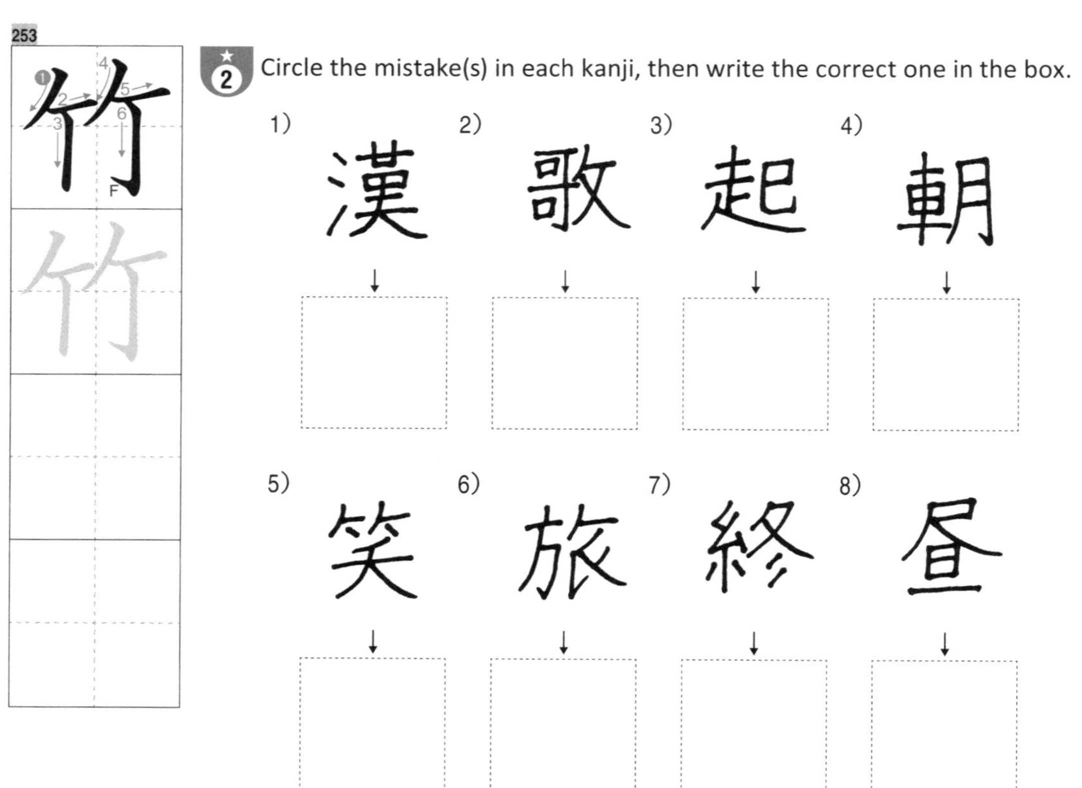

2 Circle the mistake(s) in each kanji, then write the correct one in the box.

Class: ________ Name: ____________

3 Complete kanji 1)-10) by adding an element from the box below. Then provide their readings in (　).
You may use the same element more than once.

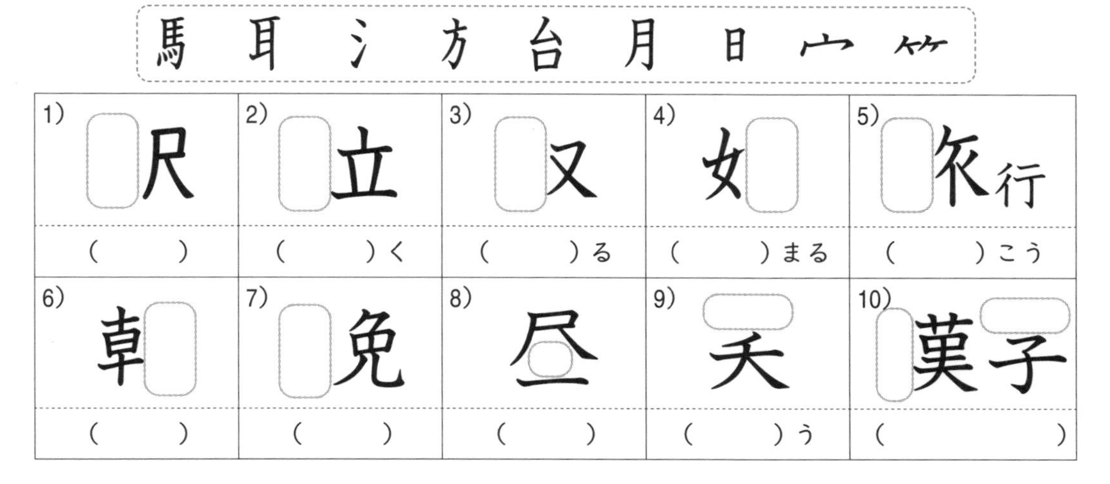

4 For each picture, fill in (　) with the corresponding word using kanji from this lesson. Use the dictionary form and add *okurigana* as necessary.

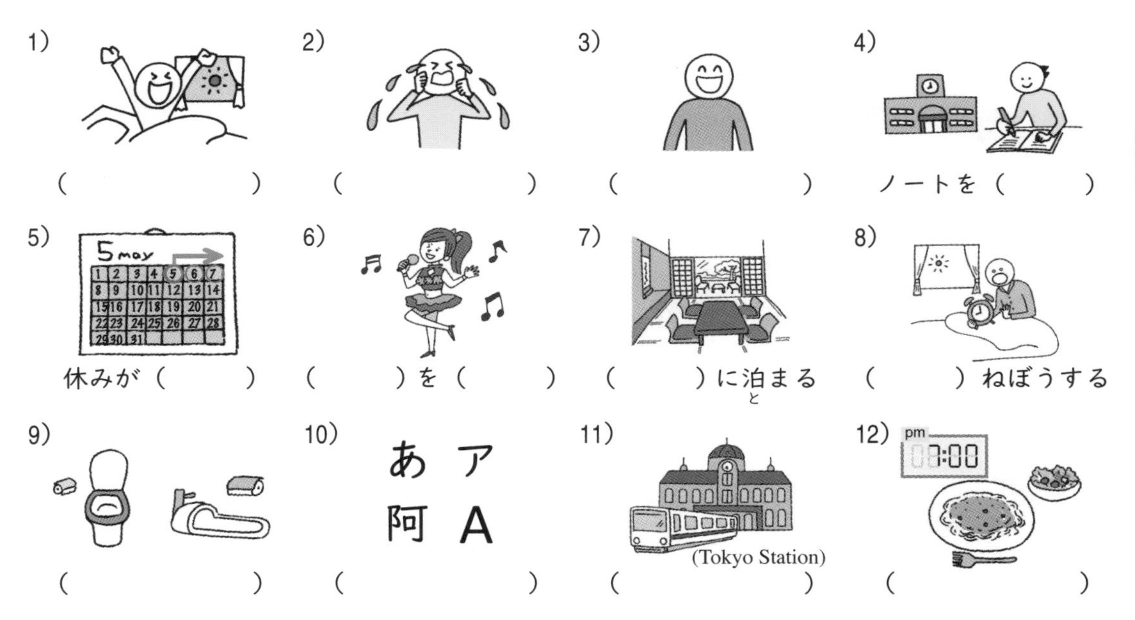

5 Choose the correct combination of kanji and its *okurigana*.

1) いい仕事が［a. 決まり　b. 決り］ました。とてもうれしいです。

2) 旅行のスケジュールを早く［a. 決めて　b. 決て］ください。

3) 会議(かいぎ)は10時に［a. 始じまって　b. 始まって　c. 始って］、11時に［a. 終わり　b. 終り］ます。

4) 先週からヨガを［a. 始じめ　b. 始め　c. 始］ました。

5) 毎朝８時に［a. 起きて　b. 起て］います。

6) 明日の朝７時に［a. 起こして　b. 起して　c. 起て］ください。

7) クラスで日本の歌を［a. 歌たい　b. 歌い］ました。

Lesson 16

Class: ________ Name: ____________

6 Circle the most appropriate word from a.-d. to complete each sentence, then write its reading in __.

1）８時に映画が________から、７時５０分に映画館の前で会いましょう。

a. 終わります　b. 始まります　c. 始めます　d. 取ります

2）漢字テストで100点(てん)を________。

a. 笑いました　b. 決めました　c. 取りました　d. 洗いました

3）宿題が________から、ゲームをしようと思います。

a. 終わって　b. 始まって　c. 歌って　d. 取って

4）明日、７時のバスに乗るから、________起きなくてはいけません。

a. 毎晩　b. 今朝　c. 夜遅く　d. 朝早く

5）旅行のスケジュールが________ら、新幹線(しんかんせん)のチケットを買います。

a. 決めた　b. 決まった　c. 取った　d. 終わった

6）昨日はカラオケで①________り、映画を見て②________りして、楽しかったです。

① a. 決まった　b. 始まった　c. 洗った　d. 歌った

② a. 取った　b. 起きた　c. 笑った　d. 終わった

7 Provide the readings for the following words. Each word should be read in the direction that the arrow indicates.

1) → 文 字　2) ↓ 漢 字

3) ↓ 歌 う　4) → 歌 手

5) ↓ 今 朝　6) → 朝 ねぼう

7) → 親 切　8) ↓ 売り 切 れる

9) → お 手 洗い　10) ↓ 歌 手

11) ↓ 半 分　12) → 分 かる

13) → からい 味　14) ↓ 意 味

15) ↓ 旅 行　16) → 行 く

1) ________ 2) ________ 3) ________ 4) ________

5) ________ 6) ________ 7) ________ 8) ________

9) ________ 10) ________ 11) ________ 12) ________

13) ________ 14) ________ 15) ________ 16) ________

Class: ＿＿＿＿＿＿ Name: ＿＿＿＿＿＿＿＿＿＿＿＿

8 ★★ Provide the readings for kanji words and compounds a.-g. in [ ]. Then, fill in ( ) with the corresponding letter of the most appropriate word to complete each sentence.

a. お手洗い [ ]　b. 画家 [ ]　c. 出して [ ]

今日は私のおすすめの「とびら美術館(びじゅつかん)」について話します。ここでは世界中の 1)( ) の絵が見られます。でも、一番のおすすめは絵じゃないです。実(じつ)は 2)( ) のデザインがとてもユニークでおもしろいんです。それから、美術館(びじゅつかん)のカフェではとてもおいしいコーヒーを 3)( ) くれます。ぜひ、行ってみてください。

d. 親せき [ ]　e. 理由 [ ]　f. 出して [ ]　g. 旅行 [ ]

今日は『ファミリー・トリップ』という映画について話します。これは５歳(さい)の子どもが 4)( ) の人達と一緒(いっしょ)に 5)( ) する話です。おすすめの 6)( ) は、キャラクターがとてもおもしろいからです。みなさん、悲(かな)しい時、ぜひこの映画を見て、元気を 7)( ) ください！

Lesson 16

9 You are making New Year's resolutions.

★★ **Step 1** Provide the readings for the kanji of the underlined words. Note that the same kanji may have different readings depending on how it is used.

今年の目標(もくひょう) (goal; objective)

1) 日本語の授業(じゅぎょう)は９時に始まる(a.)から、毎朝(b.)、朝早く(c.) 起きなくては(d.)いけない。だから、今年は毎晩(e.)、夜遅く(f.)ゲームをしない。宿題(g.)や漢字(h.)の勉強が終わった(i.)後でゲームをする。

2) それから、健康(けんこう)のために朝ご飯(a.)は果物(くだもの)を食べて、昼ご飯(b.)と晩ご飯(c.)は野菜(やさい)をたくさん食べようと思う。

3) そして、一緒(いっしょ)に泣いたり(a.) 笑ったり(b.)できる友達(c.)をたくさん作る。それから、ナナという歌手(d.)の歌(e.)が好きな人達とつながりたい。

★★★ **Step 2** Using Step 1 as a model, write your own New Year's resolutions. Use at least five highlighted kanji words on pp. 206-208 of *TOBIRA II*.

Class: ___________ Name: ________________________

10 Provide the kanji for the underlined hiragana words. Add *okurigana* as necessary. The numbers in ( ) indicate the total number of kanji that should be provided.

私のりょこう

1）５月に母と日本の「伊勢神宮（いせじんぐう）」という神社に行った。とても大きくてゆうめいな神社だ。
a.

行くことををきめてから、歴史（れきし）をしらべたり、おかねを貯（た）めたりした。(5)
b. c. d.

2）あさはやく でんしゃでえきについて、神社に歩（ある）いて行った。かみさまにお参（まい）りする (to pray)
a. b. c. d. e.

まえに手をあらわなくてはいけなかった。それから、お参（まい）りのいちじかんご、ひるごはん
f. g. h. i.

に「伊勢（いせ）うどん」というめずらしいうどんをたべた。とてもおいしかった。(17)
j.

3）よるはりょかんに泊（と）まった。母といろいろな話をして、母のいままでのじんせいについて
a. b. c. d. e.

聞くことができた。冗談（じょうだん）をいって わらったり、悲（かな）しい経験（けいけん）を聞いてないたりした。いい
f. g. h.

よるだった。(10)

4）次のあさ、車をいちだい借（か）りて、うみに行った。車の中でうたったり、きれいな景色（けしき）を見た
a. b. c. d.

りして楽しかったけれど、まえの日はよるおそくまでおきていたから、ちょっとねむかった。
e. f. g.

(9)

5）私達の日本のりょこうは月曜日にはじまって、金曜日におわった。とても楽しかった。(4)
a. b. c.

11 Using #10 as a model, write about a recent trip of yours in detail. Use kanji that you have learned in LL3-16 as much as possible.

Class: __________ Name: ______________________

読む練習 | Reading practice

▶『とびらII』L16 読みましょう#2(p.234)を読んで、答(こた)えてください。

日本のすごいものについて書いてある記事を読んで、質問(しつもん)に答(こた)えましょう。

Understanding demonstratives: こ-words

Choose the most appropriate function between a. and b. below for the following こ-words from the article.

a. To introduce an upcoming topic

b. To refer to things the writer feels temporally, spatially, or psychologically close to

① これ (in the title) [a. b.] ②このトイレ (l.28) [a. b.] ③このすごく便利(べんり)なトイレ (l.28) [a. b.]

Identifying omitted words

1) Identify the omitted words to fill in [ ] and supplement the underlined words (a)-(c). Refer to the example on p.235 #1 of *TOBIRA II* for guidance.

l.10 (a) すばらしい日本の文化だ [ ] はすばらしい日本の文化だ

l.22 (b) 信(しん)じられている [ ] に信(しん)じられている

l.27 (c) かわかした [ ] をかわかした

Scanning

2) 留学生(りゅうがくせい)の声(こえ)を読んで、日本の駅弁(えきべん)とトイレについて分かったことを書いてください。

おどろいたもの	分かったこと（四つずつ (each)）
駅弁(えきべん)	・新幹線(しんかんせん)の中でお弁当(べんとう)を食べてもいい。 ・ ・ ・
トイレ	・ ・ ・ ・

Comprehension check

3) Insert the appropriate words in "___から___まで" to indicate the part of the sentence that modifies each boxed word.

l.6 人 __________から__________まで l.9 駅弁(えきべん) __________から__________まで

l.12 こと __________から__________まで l.21 友達 __________から__________まで

l.27 トイレ __________から__________まで

4) あなたは日本の何がどうしてすごいと思いますか。自分の考(かんが)えと理由を書いてください。

____

Lesson 16

Class: ___________ Name: ______________________

書く練習 | Writing practice

▶書くシートは「とびら初級WEBサイト」にあります。

紹介文を書く (Write an introduction to something)

Task：Write about something exclusive or unique to your country/culture that you think would impress people from other countries/cultures (Ex. food, drinks, daily life items, architecture, vehicles, books, songs).

1 **Pre-writing activity:** Brainstorm your ideas and create an outline using simple keywords or phrases.

紹介したい物

紹介したい物

国や文化

絵か写真

④ 最後に言いたいこと

① 紹介したい物について話したいこと (facts) を３つ

②それを紹介する理由

③ 紹介したい物について自分の経験や考え

2 **Writing:** Using the outline above, write your introduction. Organize the content from ① to ④ to make your introduction flow more naturally.

Checklist

✓	Use the です・ます forms.
✓	Write a minimum of six sentences with a clear introduction, body, and conclusion.
✓	When explaining your topic, use passive sentences with the thing as the subject. （例：〇〇は～によって作られました。）
✓	Use as many learned kanji as possibe.
✓	Use as many grammar points as possible from the box below.

☐ [Thing] は（[Person] によって）V (passive)
☐ ～て [Reason]
☐ ～しか～ない
☐ ～ばよかった
☐ V つもり
☐ Noun modification clauses
☐ ～し～し
☐ ～たら

Exit Check

Now go back to the Kanji List for this lesson (p.56) and do the exit check to see what kanji you can read and write.

Class: ___________ Name: ______________________

漢字の復習(ふくしゅう)(2) ｜ Kanji Review (2) [Lessons 14-16]

✎ 14課(か)から16課(か)で新しく習(なら)った漢字の復習(ふくしゅう)をしましょう。全部(ぜんぶ)読んだり書いたりできますか。読み方や書き方が分からない漢字には○をして、よく復習(ふくしゅう)しましょう。

The highlighted kanji words include new readings for kanji you've already learned.

Nouns	＜もの＞ 自転車　薬　火　服　水着　宿題　問題　試験　消しゴム　ご飯　朝ご飯　昼ご飯　晩ご飯　字　漢字　文字 ＜人＞ 医者　歌手　家族 ＜所＞ (お)店　本屋　部屋　教会　教室　映画館　大使館　図書館　旅館　駅　お手洗い　入口／入り口　出口 ＜時＞ 朝　今朝　毎朝　昼　夕方　夜　晩　今晩　毎晩 ＜その他(ほか) (other)＞ 野球部(やきゅうぶ)　味　意見　心　方言　歌　お化け
Verbs	(～を)開ける　閉める　消す　汚す　助ける　起こす　始める　決める　運ぶ　動かす　続ける　調べる　忘れる　受ける　習う　取る　歌う　洗う　運転する　練習する ｜ (～を／に)旅行する ｜ (～に)乗る　乗り遅れる　遅れる　質問する ｜ (～に～を)教える ｜ (～が)開く　閉まる　消える　困る　汚れる　助かる　起きる　始まる　決まる　転ぶ　足りる　終わる　泣く　笑う　運動する　朝ねぼう(を)する
Adjs.	汚い　遅い　痛い
Advs.	朝早く　夜遅く
Other	最悪　半分　～台

✎ 上の漢字をできるだけたくさん使って、「場所」の漢字マップを作ってみましょう。

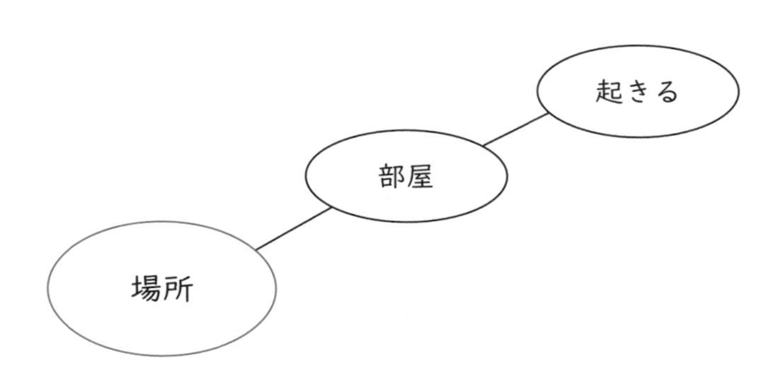

Lesson 16

Lesson 17 お店を手伝わせていただけませんか。

てつだ

Won't you let me help out around the shop?

Kanji List できるCheck ☑

	254	255	256	257	258	259	260	261	262	263	264	265	266	267	268	269	270	271	272
Kanji	北	南	西	合	送	活	近	歩	急	授	卒	業	写	真	研	究	顔	幸	正
Entry Check																			
Exit Check																			

Kanji story Kanji for the four cardinal directions (north, south, east, and west) are represented by the kanji stories below. Read the hints and guess which direction is being depicted in each kanji picture.

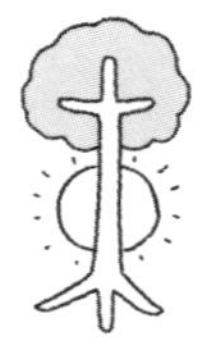

The sun rises behind the tree.

When the sun goes down, the bird returns to its nest.

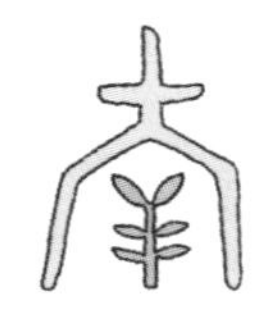

Plants grow tall in warmer climates.

Two people huddle with their backs together for warmth.

School photo album Which kanji can you recognize?

Class: ____________ Name: ______________________________

漢字の練習 | Kanji practice

1 Trace the gray kanji first, then write each kanji twice as neatly as possible.

S=stop F=flick R=release C=curved line ↓→=direction ◯=note ◌=space

254	255	256	257	258	259
北	南	西	合	送	活
北	南	西	合	送	活

260	261	262	263	264	265
近	歩	急	授	卒	業
近	歩	急	授	卒	業

long short

Lesson 17

Class: ________ Name: ______________

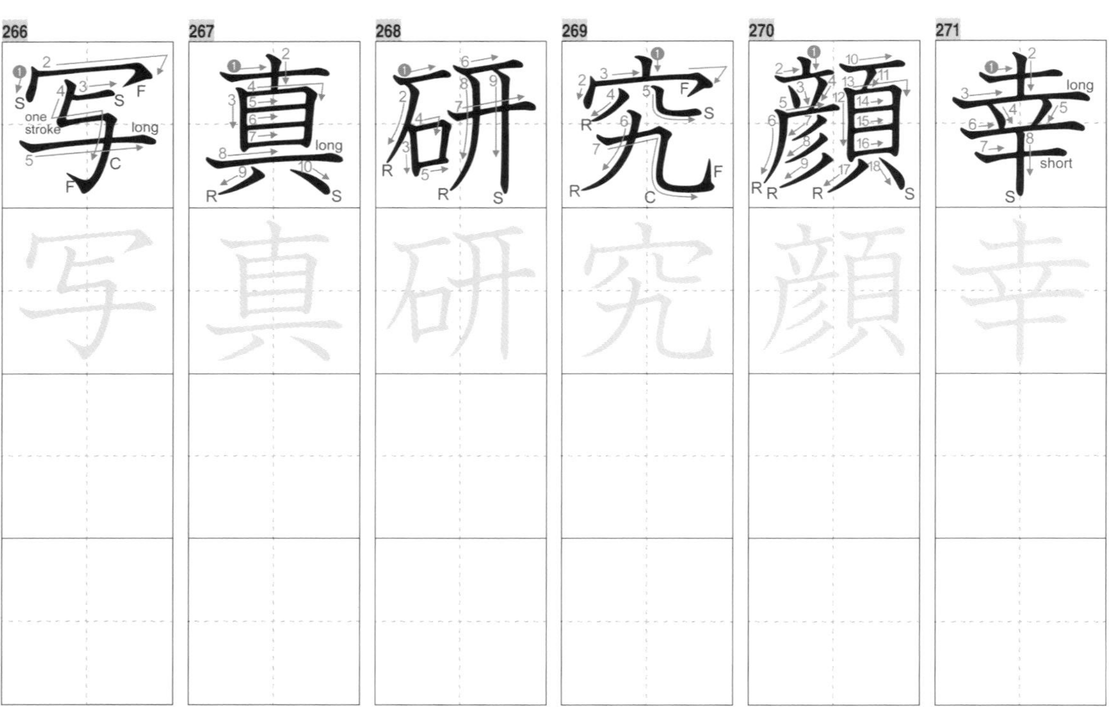

272

正

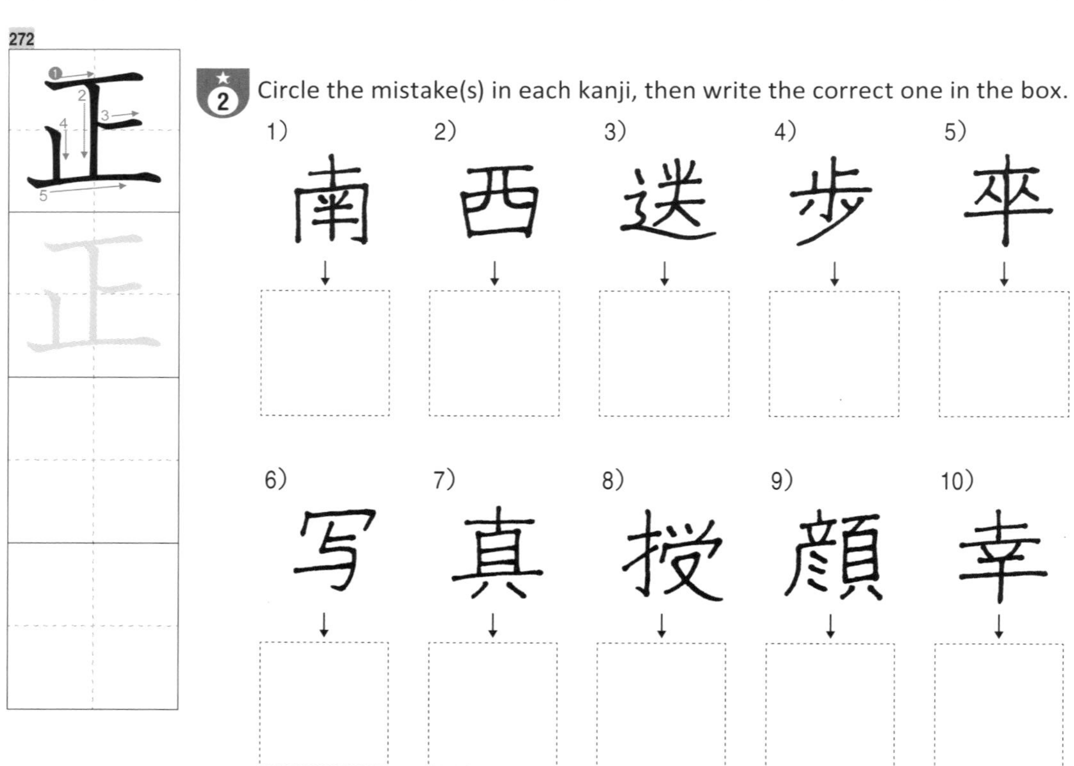

Class: ＿＿＿＿＿＿　Name: ＿＿＿＿＿＿＿＿＿＿＿＿

3 Circle the part(s) in each printed kanji that differ from its handwritten version.

Ex.

1)

2)

3)

4 Complete kanji 1)-7) by adding an element from the box below. Then, fill in the table with a word using that kanji and its reading as shown in the example. You may use the same element more than once.

罒	十	入	冖	穴	亠	止

Ex.	1)	2)	3)	4)	5)	6)	7)
業	少	竿	九	平	用	与	口
授業							
じゅぎょう							

5 Choose the correct combination of kanji and its *okurigana*.

1) このワークブックで［a. 正い　b. 正しい］漢字の書き方を［a. 学んで　b. 学なんで］ください。

2) 台風(たいふう)が［a. 近て　b. 近いて　c. 近づいて］いますから、［a. 急で　b. 急いで　c. 急そいで］家に帰ってください。［a. 歩て　b. 歩いて　c. 歩るいて］帰る人は車に気をつけてくださいね。

3) 祖父(そふ)は亡(な)くなるまで健康(けんこう)で、［a. 幸せ　b. 幸わせ　c. 幸あわせ］に［a. 生た　b. 生きた］と思う。

4) 引(ひ)っ越(こ)しをした友達が新しい住所(じゅうしょ)を［a. 知せる　b. 知らせる］メールを［a. 送て　b. 送って　c. 送くって］くれた。

6 Provide the readings for the words 1)-6) in ( ), then match each word with its explanation on the right.

1) 西口　(　　　　　　)・　　　　・大学の先生

2) 授業料　(　　　　　　)・　　　　・駅の西にある出口

3) 教授　(　　　　　　)・　　　　・一月一日から七日まで

4) 最近　(　　　　　　)・　　　　・勉強するために払(はら)うお金

5) 卒業　(　　　　　　)・　　　　・ちょっと前から今まで

6) 正月　(　　　　　　)・　　　　・学ぶことが全部(ぜんぶ)終わって学校を出ること

Class: ___________ Name: _________________________

7 Provide the reading for kanji words and compounds a.-i. in __. Then, fill in (   ) with the corresponding letter of the most appropriate word to complete each sentence.

a. 人間 ________ b. 日本食 ________ c. 世話 ________ d. 大雪 ________ e. 学長 ________
f. 天国 ________ g. しめ切り ________ h. 学ぶ ________ i. 役(やく)に立つ ________

1) 卒業式(しき) (ceremony) では、最初に大学の（　　）がスピーチをした。

2) 祖母(そぼ)はいつも、死んだ人は（　　）に行って、幸せになるんだよと言っていた。

3)（　　）で飛行機(ひこうき)がキャンセルになったから、出張(しゅっちょう)に行けなかった。

4) 日本に来た外国人の観光客(かんこうきゃく)は、たいてい（　　）が好きになるようだ。

5) 会社に入った時にお（　　）になった部長が亡(な)くなったと聞いて、驚(おどろ)いた。

6) 日本語の色々な表現(ひょうげん)について意味や使い方を（　　）のは、とてもおもしろい。

7) レポートの（　　）は明日だから、今日メールで送った。

8) このアプリは漢字の正しい読み方がすぐに見つかるから、便利(べんり)で（　　）。

9) アイさんは、にゃんたは（　　）の言葉(ことば)が分かると思っているようだ。

8 Fill in __ with the appropriate kanji to identify the given region or direction. For 3)-5), provide their readings in (   ). (Use the visual clues and refer to p.60 and p.244 of *TOBIRA II* for words you do not know.)

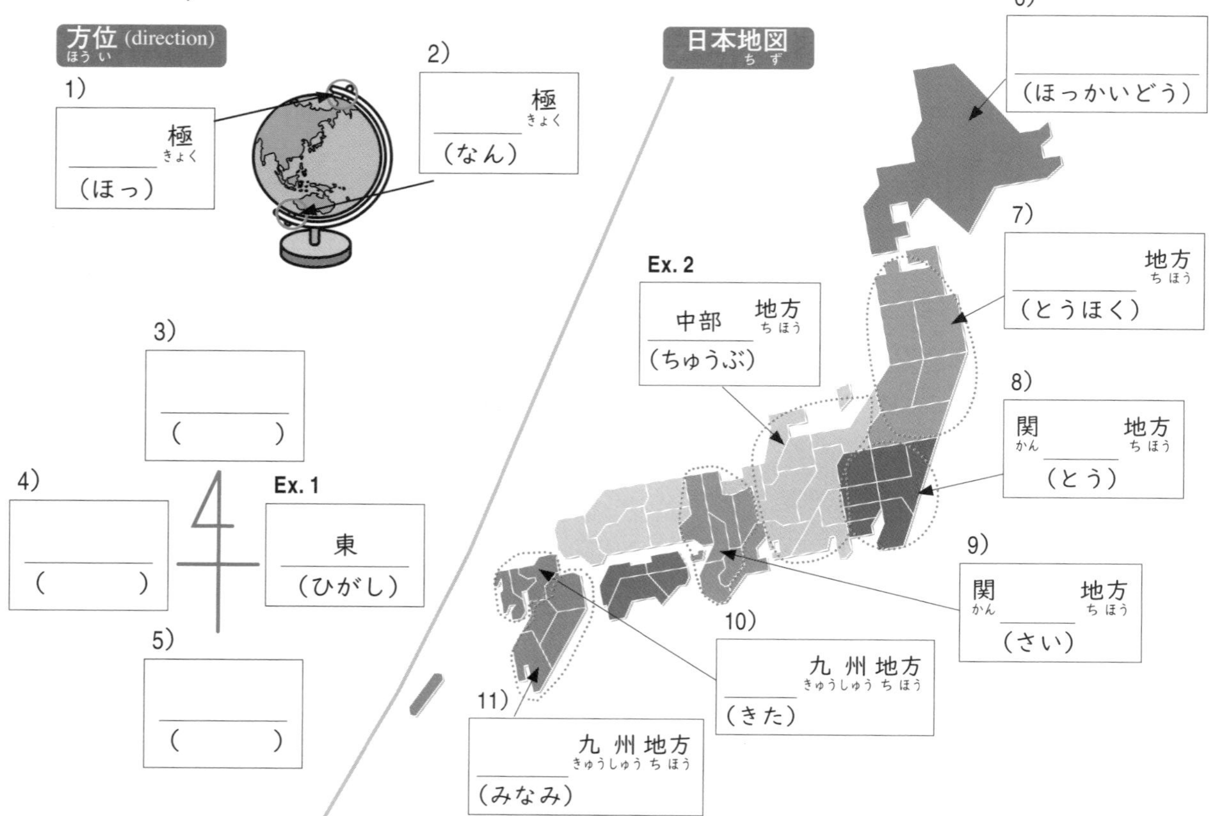

Class: __________ Name: ____________________

9 For each kanji compound, provide the meanings of the individual kanji. Then, write your guess for the meaning of the kanji compound as in the example. (Refer to p.60 and p.248 of *TOBIRA II*.)

Ex. 南風(みなみかぜ)	南 + 風 [south] [wind] = [south wind]
1) 北風(きたかぜ)	北 + 風 [ ] [ ] = [ ]
2) 東南(とうなん)アジア	東 + 南 + アジア [ ] [ ] [ ] = [ ]
3) 笑顔(えがお)	笑 + 顔 [ ] [ ] = [ ]
4) 泣(な)き顔(がお)	泣き + 顔 [ ] [ ] = [ ]
5) 顔色(かおいろ)	顔 + 色 [ ] [ ] = [ ]
6) 急行(きゅうこう)電車	急 + 行 + 電車 [ ] [ ] [ ] = [ ]
7) 送料(そうりょう)	送 + 料 [ ] [ ] = [ ]
8) 送金(そうきん)	送 + 金 [ ] [ ] = [ ]
9) 近道(ちかみち)	近 + 道 [ ] [ ] = [ ]
10) 真夜中(まよなか)	真 + 夜 + 中 [ ] [ ] [ ] = [ ]

10 Provide the readings for the kanji of the underlined words. Note that the same kanji may have different readings depending on how it is used.

1) つめを切っている(a.)時に急に(b.)くしゃみが出て(c.)、指(ゆび)をちょっと切ってしまった。痛い(d.)…

2) 仕事(a.)で外国人(b.)のお客(きゃく)様(c.)と会話(d.)する時は、簡単(かんたん)で正しい(e.)文法(ぶんぽう)を使って(f.)話した(g.)方(h.)がいいです。

3) お正月(a.)に神社(b.)にお参(まい)りに行ったら、部長(c.)とご家族(d.)に会った(e.)ので、一緒(いっしょ)に写真(f.)をとった。

4) 人間(a.)や動物(b.)が平和(へいわ)に生きられる(c.)環境(かんきょう)について話し合い(d.)ましょう。

5) 東京(a.)の新宿(しんじゅく)駅の出口(b.)には、中央(ちゅうおう)口、東口(c.)、西口(d.)、南口(e.)があります。

世界で一番(f.)人(g.)が多(おお)い駅(h.)で、一日(i.)に約(やく) (about) 350万人(j.)も利用(りよう)する (to utilize) そうです。

Class: ______ Name: ____________

11 Provide the kanji for the underlined hiragana words. Add *okurigana* as necessary. The numbers in ( ) indicate the total number of kanji that should be provided.

四年間の思い出

1) 大学せいかつでいろいろなことをまなべてよかった。(5)
a. b. c.

2) 健康(けんこう)のためにバスにのらないで、まいにち、あるいて学校に行った。でも、おおゆきが降(ふ)った時はバスで行った。(6)
a. b. c. d.

3) 遠(とお)くにあるきょうしつでグループけんきゅうがある時は、いそがないとまにあわないから、よくはしった。(8)
a. b. c. d. e.

4) 日本ぶんかを紹介(しょうかい)するかつどうで、しょうがっこうでしょどうをおしえるボランティアをした。子ども達のうれしそうなかおがわすれられない。(12)
a. b. c. d. e. f. g.

5) みんなでeスポーツのしあいにでたのは、とてもたのしかったけれど、つぎの日が日本語のさくぶんのしめきりだったので、しあいのあいだにかかなくてはいけなかった。(10)
a. b. c. d. e. f. g. h.

6) 大学のじゅぎょうりょうがたかかったので、奨学金(しょうがくきん)が少(すこ)しもらえてたすかった。(5)
a. b. c.

7) 日本でホームステイをした時、おしょうがつにきものをきてしゃしんをとってもらった。スマホにホストファミリーがおくってくれたしゃしんが入っている。(8)
a. b. c. d. e.

8) そつぎょうするひがちかづいた時、おせわになったきょうじゅにお礼(れい)をいいに、けんきゅうしつに寄(よ)った。(12)
a. b. c. d. e. f. g.

12 Using #11 as a model, write about your time in school using the title "__年間の思い出." (Insert your own number in __.) Use kanji that you have learned in LL3-17 as much as possible.

Class: ____________ Name: ____________________

読む練習 | Reading practice

▶『とびら II』L17 読みましょう#2(p.274)を読んで、答えてください。

「鈴木教授の幸せな生活」というショートストーリーを読んで、質問に答えましょう。

Identifying omitted words

1) Who did what in the story, and to whom? Insert the appropriate character from P, R, and S into each ( ).

P＝鈴木教授　**R**＝ロボット　**S**＝学生

- l.3 Ex.(**P**)はAIロボットを作りました
- l.4 (a)(　)は何もしなくてもいい
- l.5 (b)ロボットが(　)を起こしてくれます
- l.5 (c)(　)が(　)の顔を洗って
- ll.5-6 (d)(　)にご飯を食べさせてくれます
- l.6 (e)(　)が(　)の服を着がえさせて
- l.7 (f)(　)が仕事が終わる
- l.7 (g)(　)が(　)を迎えに来てくれます
- l.8 (h)(　)が(　)の手と足のつめも切ってくれる
- ll.11-12 (i)(　)は毎日肉しか食べません
- ll.12-13 (j)(　)が大学から帰ってくる
- l.20 (k)(　)が(　)の肩に手を置く

Sorting information

2) このロボットができることに○、できないことに×を入れてください。

(　　) 色々な家事をする　(　　) 体のためにいい食べ物かどうか分かる

(　　) お弁当を作る　(　　) 何かを運ぶ　(　　) 車を運転する

(　　) 部屋の温度をコントロールする　(　　) 悲しくて泣く

Understanding metaphors

3) 次のメタファー表現はどんな意味だと思いますか。コンテクストをよく考えて意味を書いてください。

l.9 バラ色になる(なりました)

意味：________________________________

l.20 氷のように冷たい

意味：________________________________

l.25 天国に行ける

意味：________________________________

Comprehension check

4) 正しい文(sentence)には○、正しくない文には×を入れてください。

(　　) 鈴木教授は、自分でできることはロボットにさせないで、全部自分でした。

(　　) 大学の食堂のランチには魚や野菜が入っているようだ。

(　　) 鈴木教授はロボットと生活して、とても幸せだったようだ。

(　　) ロボットは、鈴木教授が眠っている間に亡くなったことを知っていた。

5) このストーリーを書いた人は何が言いたいと思いますか。

Lesson 17

Class: ____________ Name: ______________________________

書く練習 | Writing practice

▶書くシートは「とびら初級WEBサイト」にあります。

自分のロボットを作ろう

タスク：Describe an AI robot that you'd like to build, including what it does, who it would help, and why you'd like to build it.

1 **Pre-writing activity:** Brainstorm your ideas and create an outline using simple keywords or phrases.

① ロボットの名前・イラスト	② 何のためのロボット？ 〈例〉～をよくする、～(の)を助ける
	③ どんなことをさせたい？
	④ どうしてそれをさせたい？
⑤ 最後に言いたいこと 〈例〉将来このロボットが作れると思うか。もしこのロボットが本当に作れたら、将来何に使われると思うか／使ってほしいか。	

2 **Writing:** Using the outline above, write about the AI robot you'd like to build. Organize the content from ① to ⑤ to make your ideas flow more naturally.

Checklist

✓	Use the です・ます forms.
✓	Be creative and describe what your robot does in detail with an interesting story.
✓	Write three or more paragraphs with minimum of eight sentences.
✓	Use as many learned kanji as possible.
✓	Use as many grammar points as possible from the box below.

☐ ～ので　☐ Causative forms　☐ V-*te* (causative) {あげる／くれる／もらう}
☐ ～か(かどうか) [Embedded question]　☐ ～と [Conditional]　☐ ～といいと思う　☐ ～ために
☐ V まで／までに　☐ V-*te* {あげる／くれる／もらう}　☐ ～しか～ない　☐ V ないで

Exit Check ☑

Now go back to the Kanji List for this lesson (p.66) and do the exit check to see what kanji you can read and write.

COLUMN

3

多読をしてみよう

みなさんは本を読むのが好きですか。「多読」をしてみませんか。「多読」の「多」の意味は「たくさん」、「読」の意味は「読む」です。だから、「多読」の意味は「たくさん本を読むこと」です。(『とびらⅡ』Unit 5 チャレンジ #1 (p.277)を見てください)「日本語多読道場」という多読のウェブサイトから読み物を選んで読んでみましょう。使い方は巻末 (back cover) を見てください。

多読にはルールがありますか。

はい、ルールが4つあります。

① 簡単な本から読む
② 辞書を使わない
③ 分からない所は飛ばす (to skip)
④ 本が難しい時やつまらない時は他の本を読む

どんな本を読みますか。どんなレベルの本がいいですか。

色々な本を読みましょう。短い読み物、小説 (novel)、絵本、まんが、エッセイ、雑誌、何でもいいです。最初はやさしいレベルの本から始めましょう。一番大切なことは「本を読むのを楽しむこと」ですから、色々な本を楽しんで読んでください。

読んだ後、何をしますか。

色々なことをします。例えば、本の記録 (record) を書く、クラスメートと読んだ本について話す、みんなにおすすめの本を紹介するなど (and so on) です。本の記録には読んだ日、本の名前、作者、本のレベル、好きな言葉やフレーズ、感想 (reflection) などを書くといいです。

それから、自分で話を書くのもいいです。自由に短い話を書いて、他の人とシェアしてみましょう。

おもしろそうですね。多読にチャレンジしてみたいです。

はい、ぜひやってみてください。写真や絵、音声 (audio recording) も使って本の世界を楽しんでください。本を読んだり、会話をしたりするのが上手になります。漢字にも強くなりますよ。

→多読のウェブサイト：「日本語多読道場」https://yomujp.com
「にほんごたどく」https://tadoku.org/japanese/

Lesson 17

Lesson 18 好きなことをしなさい。

Do what you like.

Kanji List できるCheck ☑

	273	274	275	276	277	278	279	280	281	282	283	284	285	286	287	288	289	290	291
Kanji	院	通	考	答	残	留	重	便	利	不	弱	用	地	球	野	空	港	両	他
Entry Check																			
Exit Check																			

Kanji elements

Below are kanji introduced up to L18, sorted by elements they have in common. Those in bold are new kanji introduced in this lesson.

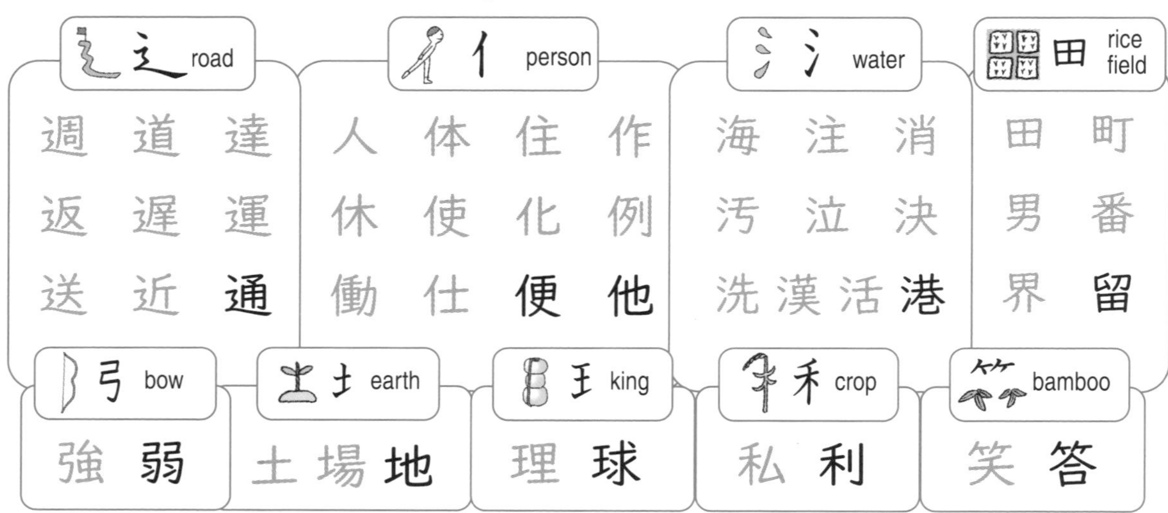

Kanji in daily life

Which kanji can you recognize?

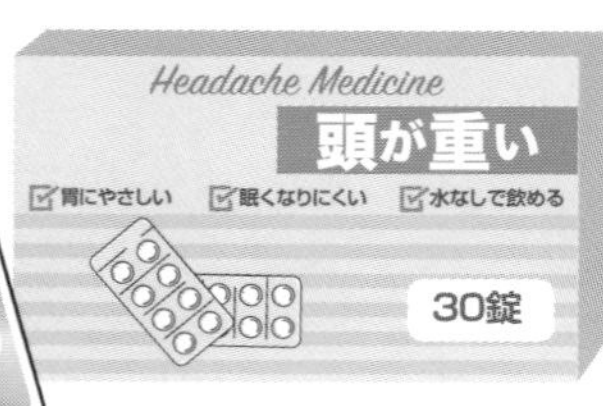

Class: ____________ Name: ______________________

漢字の練習 | Kanji practice

1 Trace the gray kanji first, then write each kanji twice as neatly as possible.

S=stop F=flick R=release C=curved line ↓ → =direction ◯=note ◌=space

273	274	275	276	277	278
院	通	考	答	残	留

279	280	281	282	283	284
重	便	利	不	弱	用

Lesson 18

Class: ＿＿＿＿＿　Name: ＿＿＿＿＿＿＿＿＿＿

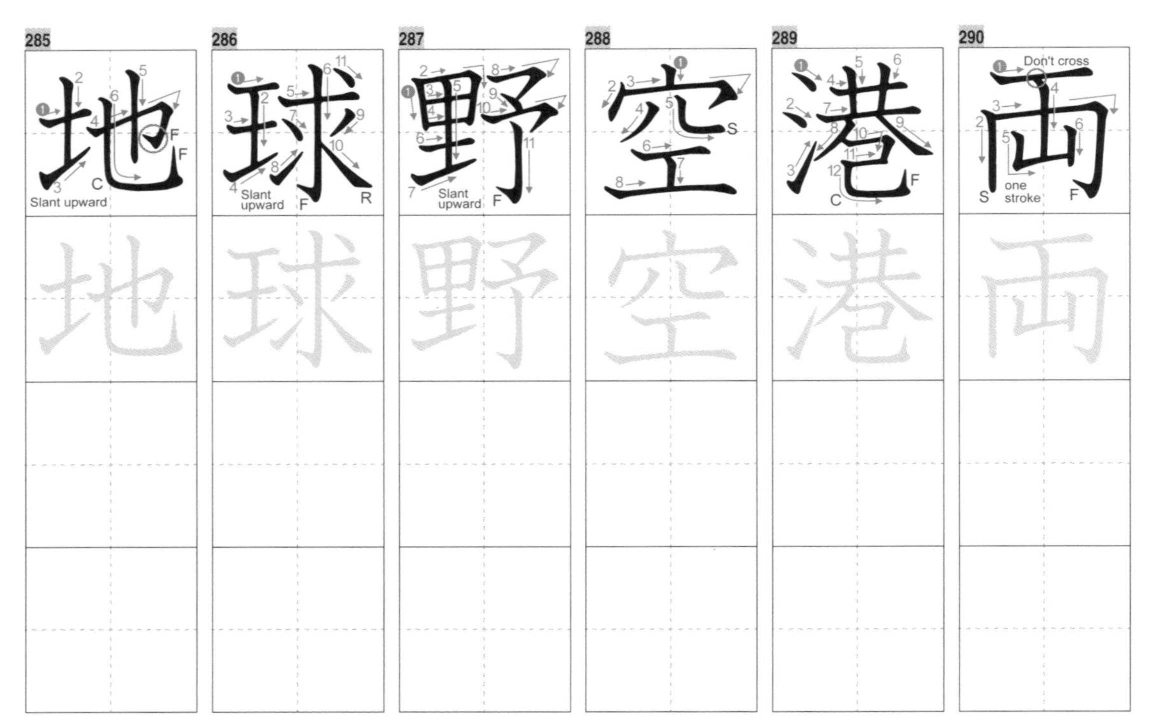

285
地
Slant upward
286
球
Slant upward
287
野
Slant upward
288
空
289
港
290
両
Don't cross
one stroke
291
他

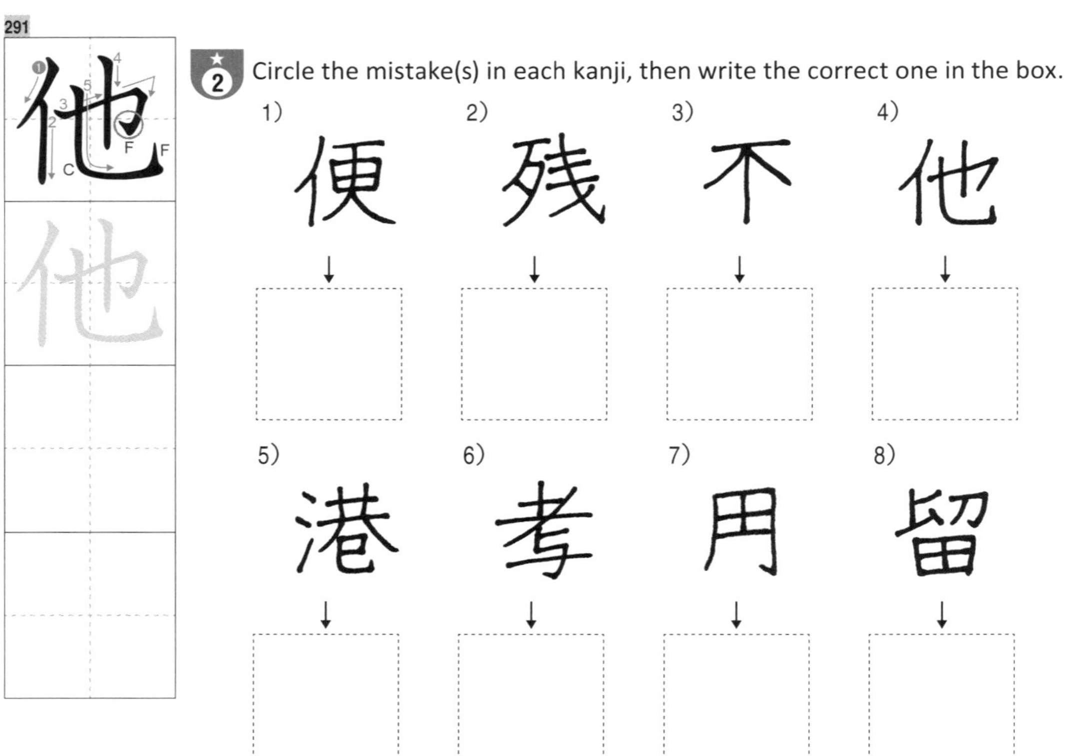

2
Circle the mistake(s) in each kanji, then write the correct one in the box.
1) 便
2) 残
3) 不
4) 他
5) 港
6) 考
7) 用
8) 留

Class: ________ Name: ______________

3 For each picture, write the corresponding kanji or kanji compound in __, then provide its reading in ( ).

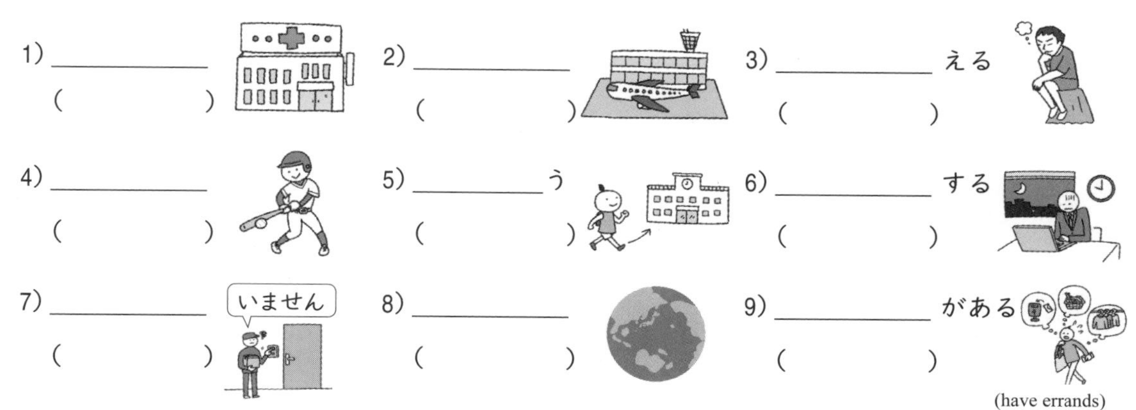

1) ______ (　　　)
2) ______ (　　　)
3) ______ える (　　　)
4) ______ (　　　)
5) ______ う (　　　)
6) ______ する (　　　)
7) ______ (　　　)
8) ______ (　　　)
9) ______ がある (　　　)

(have errands)

4 Your dog has chewed up your kanji flash cards! Make new flash cards and provide their readings in ( ) as in the example.

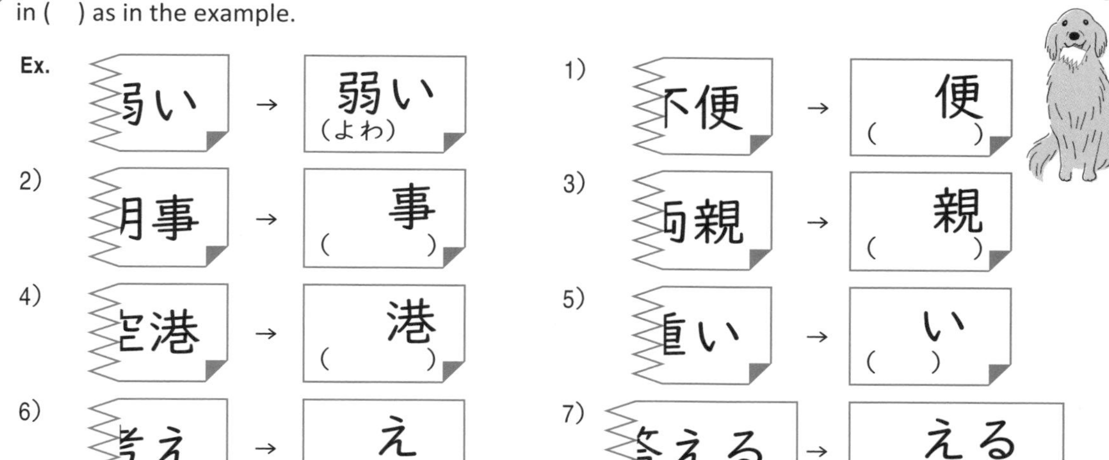

Ex. 弓い → 弱い（よわ）
1) 下便 → 　便 (　　)
2) 月事 → 　事 (　　)
3) 両親 → 　親 (　　)
4) 空港 → 　港 (　　)
5) 重い → 　い (　　)
6) 考え → 　え (　　)
7) 答える → 　える (　　)

5 Make kanji by combining one element each from A (left element) and B (right element). Then, insert the appropriate kanji in the boxes to complete the words and phrases in 1)-5). Provide their readings in ( ).

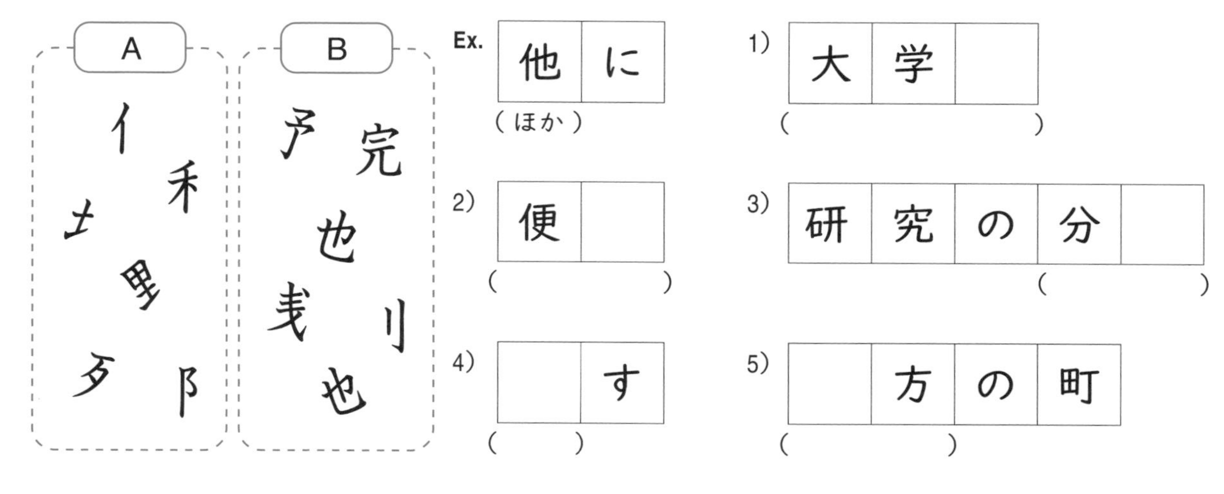

A: 亻 禾 土 里 歹 阝

B: 予 完 也 戋 刂 也

Ex. | 他 | に |（ほか）

1) | 大 | 学 | 　 | (　　　)

2) | 便 | 　 | (　　　)

3) | 研 | 究 | の | 分 | 　 | (　　　)

4) | 　 | す | (　　)

5) | 　 | 方 | の | 町 | (　　　)

Class: ___________ Name: ___________

6 Choose the appropriate reading from a.-d. for the following words.

1）留学 [a. りゅうがく b. るうがく c. りょうがく d. りゅがく]
2）病院 [a. びよういん b. びょいん c. びょういん d. びよいん]
3）空港 [a. くこ b. くこう c. くうこ d. くうこう]
4）両親 [a. りょうしん b. りょしん c. りようしん d. りよしん]
5）不便 [a. ふうべん b. ふぶん c. ふびん d. ふべん]
6）残業 [a. ざんぎょ b. さんぎょう c. ざんぎょう d. ざんごう]

7 Provide the readings for the kanji of the underlined words. Note that the same kanji may have different readings depending on how it is used.

1）A：下(a.)の駐車場(ちゅうしゃじょう) (parking lot) で待(ま)っています。
B：地下(b.)一階(いっかい)ですね。分かりました。

2）留学(a.)している間、家をずっと留守(b.)にしたくないから、誰(だれ)かに貸(か)そうと思う。

3）今日の仕事は明日まで残したくない(a.)から、残業(b.)して終わらせてしまおう。

4）黒田(くろだ)さんは長野(a.)の出身(しゅっしん)で、野球(b.)が好きだ。年(c.)は来年(d.)二十歳(はたち)になるそうだ。

5）青(あお)い空(a.)の下で空手(b.)を練習するのは気持ちがいい。

6）この図書館(a.)はこの地図(b.)にない。

7）楽しみ(a.)ながら、楽に(b.)漢字を学べる勉強のし方を知っていますか。

8）経済(けいざい)の授業(じゅぎょう)の教科書(きょうかしょ)は高いけれど、日本語の教科書(きょうかしょ)は安い(a.)ので、安心(b.)した。

9）その時間(a.)のバスに乗ったら、コンサートに間に合わない(b.)よ。

10）A：この歌、すごくいいね。今年人気が出そうだ(a.)ね。
B：うん、私も好き。声(こえ)に出して(b.)歌うと元気になるよ。

11）A：後で僕(ぼく)の部屋(a.)に遊(あそ)びにくる？
B：この宿題が終わってから行くよ。でも、この最後の部分(b.)がよく分からないんだ。

12）三行目(a.)の「東京に行く(b.)」と書いてある文から読んでください。

Class: ________ Name: ________________

8 Provide the readings for the kanji words and compounds in ＿. Then, categorize their corresponding letters into the given groups.

a. 気がつく ________	b. 分野 ________	c. 弱い ________
d. 便利（な）________	e. 守る ________	f. 答え ________
g. 地下 ________	h. 出会う ________	i. 重い ________
j. 大学院生 ________	k. 広げる ________	l. 空 ________

名詞（めいし）	形容詞（けいようし）	動詞（どうし）

9 Write the opposites of the following words in kanji. Then, provide their readings in (　). Add *okurigana* as necessary.

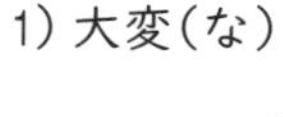
1) 大変(な)  ________ (　　　)

2) 強い  ________ (　　　)

3) 便利(な)  ________ (　　　)

4) 軽い（かる） 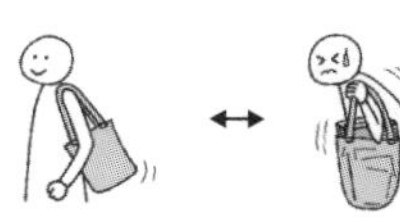 ________ (　　　)

5) 質問する  ________ (　　　)

6) 遅れる  ________ (　　　)

7) 始め 

________ (　　　)

8) 不安（ふあん）(な)  ________ (　　　)

9) 都合（つごう）がいい 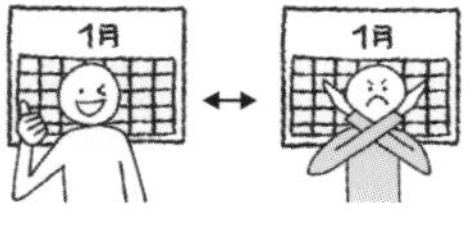

都合（つごう）が________ (　　　)

9) 退院（たいいん）する (be discharged from the hospital) 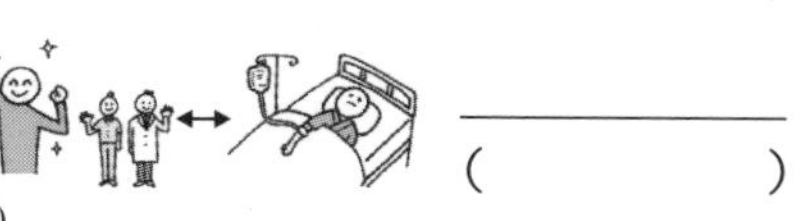 ________ (　　　)

10 Provide the readings for words 1)-6) and underlined words 7)-9) in (　), then match each word with its explanation on the right.

1) 考え (　　　　　　　　　) ・　　　・二人の親

2) 野球 (　　　　　　　　　) ・　　　・アイデア

3) 両親 (　　　　　　　　　) ・　　　・決められた時間に遅れないこと

4) 地下 (　　　　　　　　　) ・　　　・地面（じめん） (ground) の下

5) 地図 (　　　　　　　　　) ・　　　・場所を調べる時に見る物

6) 間に合う (　　　　　　　　　) ・　　　・心配がなくなること

7) <u>入院</u>する (　　　　　　　　　) ・　　　・他の国に勉強しに行くこと

8) <u>留学</u>する (　　　　　　　　　) ・　　　・バットとボールを使って九人でするスポーツ

9) <u>安心</u>する (　　　　　　　　　) ・　　　・病気やけがをして病院に一日以上（いじょう） (or more) いること

Lesson 18

Class: __________ Name: ______________________

11 ★★ Provide the kanji and their *okurigana* for words a.-f. in __. Then, fill in (　) with the corresponding letter of the most appropriate word to complete each sentence.

a. こたえられなくて →	______________	b. よわくて →	______________
c. のこして →	______________	d. かよって →	______________
e. おもくて →	______________	f. かんがえて →	______________

1）この小テストの問題はとても難[むずか]しかった。（　　）、困った。

2）毎日自転車で学校に（　　）います。でも、雨の日はバスに乗ります。

3）スーツケースにおみやげを入れすぎて、（　　）大変だった。

4）将来[しょうらい]、どんな仕事をしたいか（　　）いますか。

5）作ってもらった料理は（　　）はいけません。全部[ぜんぶ]食べましょう。

6）私の学校の野球チームは去年[きょねん]は（　　）だめだったが、今年は違[ちが]う。

12 ★★ Provide the kanji for the underlined hiragana words. Add *okurigana* as necessary. The numbers in (　) indicate the total number of kanji that should be provided.

1）Ａ：私はかんじ[a.]がよわい[b.]んだけど、ミミさんはどうやってべんきょう[c.]してる？

　Ｂ：このアプリがべんり[d.]だよ。りゅうがくせい[e.]やだいがくいんせい[f.]もつかって[g.]るよ。（15）

2）僕[ぼく]は飛行機[ひこうき]や宇宙[うちゅう] (space) が好きで、小さい時に、よくりょうしん[a.]にくうこう[b.]に連[つ]れていってもらった。飛行機[ひこうき]のことについてしつもんし[c.]たら、父は何でもこたえて[d.]くれた。将来[しょうらい]宇宙[うちゅう]に行って、宇宙[うちゅう]からちきゅう[e.]を見てみたい。（9）

3）子どもの時、父にやきゅう[a.]をおしえて[b.]もらった。それから、「まもれない[c.]約束[やくそく]はしてはいけない」と言われた。ほか[d.]には「ご飯をのこさないで[e.]食べなさい」と言われた。（6）

Class: ＿＿＿＿＿＿　Name: ＿＿＿＿＿＿＿＿＿＿＿＿

4）まだしごとがおわっていないが、今日はようじがあって、ざんぎょうできない。(7)
a.　b.　c.　d.

5）A：学校にはどうやってかよっていますか。
a.

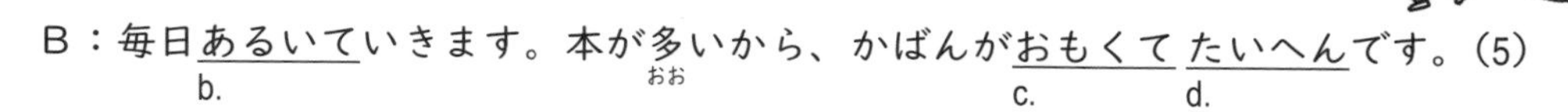

B：毎日あるいていきます。本が多(おお)いから、かばんがおもくてたいへんです。(5)
b.　c.　d.

6）日本にりゅうがくしていた時、くつしたに穴(あな)があいていることにきがつかないで、友達の家
a.　b.　c.　d.

に行ってしまった。友達のお母さんに見られてはずかしかった。(5)

13 Below is a social media post from a student who just arrived in Japan for language study. Read his story aloud, then provide the readings for the kanji of the underlined words.

日本語の勉強を始めたきっかけ（What made me want to study Japanese）

僕(ぼく)は小さい時、体が弱くてよく入院していたから、強くなるために空手を
a.　b.　c.　d.

始めました。野球やテニスもしましたが、一番好きだったのは空手です。
e.　f.

空手は心も体も強くしてくれました。その時出会った人達は、ぼくの世界を広げてく
g.　h.　i.　j.　k.

れました。他にも大事なことをたくさん学びました。空手を始めてからもっと日本の
l.　m.

ことを学びたくなって、日本語の勉強を始めました。大学で二年間日本語の授業を取っ

て、今、京都(きょうと)に留学中です。京都(きょうと)は地下鉄(ちかてつ)やバスがたくさん走っているし、地図も
n.　o.

分かりやすくて便利な町です。毎日色々なことを勉強しています。
p.

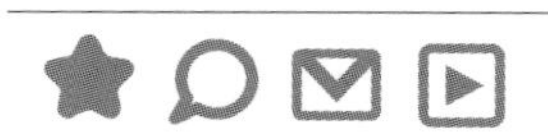

14 Using #13 as a model, write about how you started studying Japanese. Use kanji that you have learned in LL3-18 as much as possible.

Lesson 18

Class: ＿＿＿＿＿　Name: ＿＿＿＿＿＿＿＿＿＿

読む練習｜Reading practice

▶『とびら II』L18「私の世界を広げてくれた経験」(pp.311-312) を読んで、答えなさい。

中級 (intermediate) に行くための準備　４つのステップで読んでみよう

Step 1

まず、自分で読む。

Step 2

次に、「とびら初級 WEB サイト」の音声 (audio recordings) を聞く。

Step 3

それから、音声を聞きながら漢字の読み方をチェックする。

Step 4

最後に、音声と一緒に読んでみる。

読み物を読んだ後で、考えてみよう

1　[　　] の言葉を修飾している (to modify) のはどこからどこまでですか。

l.11 [ボランティア] ＿＿＿＿＿＿から＿＿＿＿＿＿まで

l.15 [病院] ＿＿＿＿＿＿から＿＿＿＿＿＿まで

l.16 [こと] ＿＿＿＿＿＿から＿＿＿＿＿＿まで

l.17 [の] ＿＿＿＿＿＿から＿＿＿＿＿＿まで

l.17 [赤ちゃん] ＿＿＿＿＿＿から＿＿＿＿＿＿まで

2　１行目から 14 行目

1）ジニーさんの子どもの時の夢は何でしたか。＿＿＿＿＿＿＿＿＿＿

2）ジニーさんはどんなことに悩んでいましたか。二つ書きなさい。

＿＿＿＿＿＿＿＿＿＿　＿＿＿＿＿＿＿＿＿＿

3）７行目：「アドバイスしてくれました」とありますが、誰がジニーさんにどんなアドバイスをしてくれましたか。

ジニーさんは悩んでいた時、＿＿＿＿＿に＿＿＿＿＿＿＿＿＿＿と言われた。

4）ジニーさんが決めたボランティアはどんなボランティアでしたか。どうしてそれに決めましたか。

＿＿＿＿＿＿＿＿＿＿＿＿＿＿＿＿＿＿＿＿

5）14 行目：「でも、実は全然楽じゃありませんでした」とありますが、どうして楽じゃなかったと思いますか。自分の考えを書きなさい。

＿＿＿＿＿＿＿＿＿＿＿＿＿＿＿＿＿＿＿＿

3　15 行目から 34 行目

1）15 行目：[そこ] はどこですか。＿＿＿＿＿＿＿＿＿＿

2）ジニーさんはどんな仕事をしましたか。＿＿＿＿＿＿＿＿＿＿

Class: ＿＿＿＿＿　Name: ＿＿＿＿＿＿＿＿＿＿

3）ジニーさんはどんな時にそのボランティアをやめたいと思いましたか。

＿＿＿＿＿＿＿＿＿＿＿＿＿＿＿＿＿＿＿＿

4）ジニーさんとまりえちゃんはどうして仲良く(なかよ)なったと思いますか。自分の考えを書きなさい。

＿＿＿＿＿＿＿＿＿＿＿＿＿＿＿＿＿＿＿＿

5）次の表現(ひょうげん)はメタファーです。どんな意味だと思いますか。日本語で答えなさい。

l.16 病気が軽い(かる)＝＿＿＿＿＿＿＿＿　l.17 重い病気＝＿＿＿＿＿＿＿＿

6）(a)～(e)は誰(だれ)がしたことですか。（　　）にJ（＝ジニーさん）、M（＝まりえちゃん）を入れなさい。

l.27	Ex. 言った	（ J ）	l.28	(a) 返事しかしませんでした	（　　）
l.29	(b) 言った	（　　）	ll.29-30	(c) 食べ始め(たはじ)ました	（　　）
l.30	(d) 笑いました	（　　）	l.32	(e) 喜(よろこ)んでいる	（　　）

7）正しい文には○を、正しくない文には×を入れなさい。

（　　）子どもの病院のボランティアは全部(ぜんぶ)難(むずか)しい仕事だった。

（　　）まりえちゃんは病院にいる間、全然(ぜんぜん)英語を話さなかった。

（　　）まりえちゃんはご飯が食べられない病気だった。

（　　）ジニーさんとまりえちゃんは今も友達で、時々会う。

④ 35行目(ぎょうめ)から43行目(ぎょうめ)

1）ジニーさんが病院のボランティアをして気がついたことは何ですか。二つ書きなさい。

＿＿＿＿＿＿＿＿＿＿　＿＿＿＿＿＿＿＿＿＿

2）ジニーさんの将来(しょうらい)の夢(ゆめ)やしたいことは何ですか。二つ書きなさい。

＿＿＿＿＿＿＿＿＿＿　＿＿＿＿＿＿＿＿＿＿

3）ジニーさんが今しているボランティアは何ですか。＿＿＿＿＿＿＿＿

4）ジニーさんは何が自分の世界を広げてくれたと思っていますか。二つ書きなさい。

＿＿＿＿＿＿＿＿＿＿　＿＿＿＿＿＿＿＿＿＿

5）ジニーさんのスピーチ原稿(げんこう)を読んで、あなたはどう思いましたか。三つの文で答えなさい。

【　】には下から接続表現(せつぞくひょうげん)を一つ選(えら)んで書きなさい。

でも　だから　それから　そして　例えば

まず、＿＿＿＿＿＿＿＿＿＿＿＿＿＿＿＿。

【　　　】、＿＿＿＿＿＿＿＿＿＿＿＿＿＿。

【　　　】、＿＿＿＿＿＿＿＿＿＿＿＿＿＿。

Lesson 18

Class: ____________ Name: ______________________

書く練習 | Writing practice

▶書くシートは「とびら初級WEBサイト」にあります。

スピーチ原稿（speech manuscript）を書く

タスク：スピーチをするために、あなたの「自分の世界を広げてくれた経験」について書きなさい。

1 **書く前に：**どんな経験があなたの世界を広げてくれたと思いますか。下の質問に答えながら、アウトラインを考えましょう。文を書かないで、キーワードやフレーズで書きなさい。

Opening	1)はじめに [a hook or an attention-grabbing phrase]
	2)世界を広げてくれた経験は何か 〈例〉アルバイト、インターンシップ、クラブ活動、留学、大変だったこと
Body	3)その経験では、いつ、どこで、どんなことをしたか
	4)その経験をした時、どんなことがあって、どう思ったか
Closing	5)その経験をして、経験する前と何がどう変わったか 〈例〉興味、行動 (action)、性格、人との関係 (relationship)、好きなもの、したいこと、考え方

2 **書く：**上のアウトラインをもとに (based on) して、スピーチ原稿を書きなさい。

Checklist

- ✓ です・ます フォームで書く。
- ✓ 6 文以上 (or more) で、3 段落で書く。
- ✓ 具体的な (specific) 話を入れる。
- ✓ 習った漢字をできるだけたくさん使う。
- ✓ 下の文法をできるだけたくさん使う。

☐ Passive forms ☐ Causative forms ☐ Causative-passive forms
☐ まだ (still) ☐ もう (no longer) ☐ ～ば ☐ ～のに ☐ ～ために
☐ ～はずだ ☐ ～たり～たりする ☐ ～て{あげる／くれる／もらう}
☐{Adj(i)-stemく／Adj(na)に／Nに}なる・する ☐ Noun modification clauses

Exit Check

Now go back to the Kanji List for this lesson (p.76) and do the exit check to see what kanji you can read and write.

COLUMN

4

おすすめの本について発表しよう

みなさんはどんな本が好きですか。自分が好きな本を他の人に紹介しましょう。(『とびら II』Unit 5 チャレンジ #1 Step 2 (p.277) を見てください)

やり方

① おすすめの本を選ぶ。

↓

② その本について発表する。

↓

③ 発表を聞いた人は、質問したりコメントしたりする。

↓

④ 発表を聞いた人は、一番読んでみたい本に投票する (to vote)。

本について

好きな本を 1 冊選ぼう！

小説 (novel)、写真集 (photo book)、まんが、図鑑 (pictorial book)、絵本、何でも OK!

発表について

その本のおすすめポイントを話そう！

話、キャラクター、イラスト、表紙 (cover)、フォント、値段、紙、何でも OK!

●発表する時

- 発表を聞いている人とコミュニケーションを取りながら発表する。
- 本の表紙 (cover) やページを見せながら発表する。
- あらすじ (story) だけ話さない。自分の気持ちも話す。
- ネタバレ (spoiler) はだめ！
- その本の好きなところやおもしろいと思う気持ちを伝える。
- 話すポイントはできるだけ少なくする。あまり色々なことを話さない。

発表会をやってみよう

どこで？

〈例〉
- クラスで
- 大学で
- コミュニティーで
- 町の図書館で
  →地域の人 (local people) とつながろう！
- オンラインで
  →色々な人とつながろう！

発表会をやる前に考えること

- 発表の時間は何分にするか。
- どうやって投票する (to vote) か。
- どうやってたくさんの人に来てもらうか。

このイベントで大切なこと

- おもしろそうな本を見つけること
- 他の人とコミュニケーションすること
- おすすめの本をシェアして、他の人にも読んでもらうこと

明日はどんな話をなさいますか。

What story will you be telling tomorrow?

Kanji List できるCheck ☑

	292	293	294	295	296	297	298	299	300	301	302	303	304	305	306	307	308	309	310
Kanji	覚	貸	借	待	落	違	死	多	少	工	主	員	去	風	経	春	夏	秋	冬
Entry Check																			
Exit Check																			

Kanji-emoji

Can you guess what kanji the following emojis represent? Try making your own kanji-emoji!

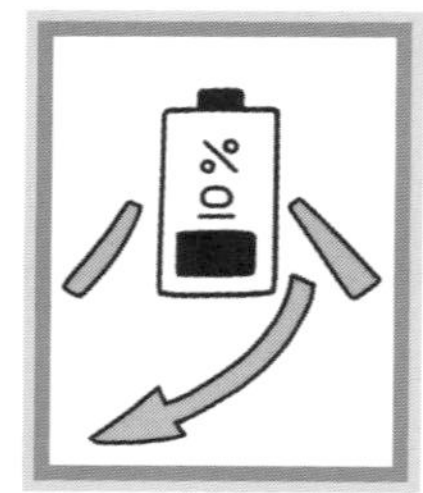

Kanji in daily life

Which kanji can you recognize?

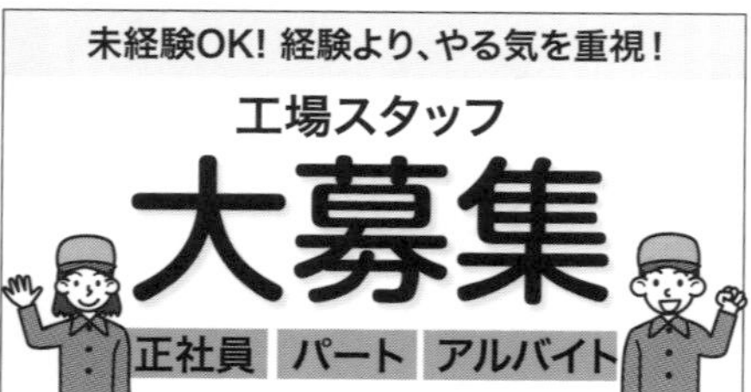

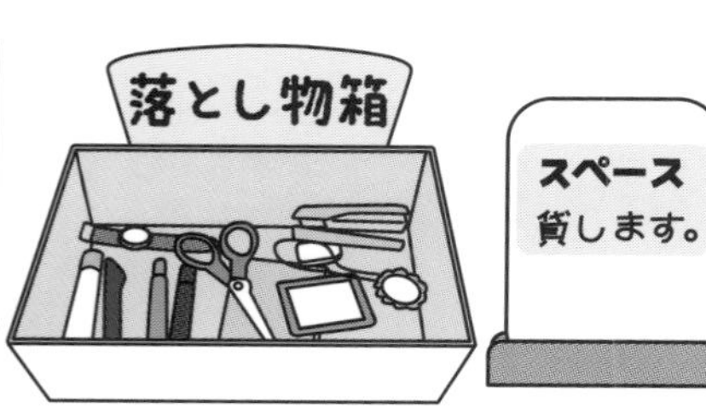

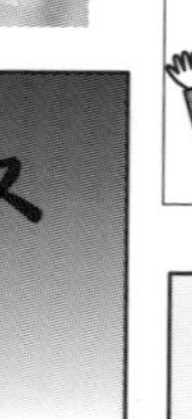

Class: ________ Name: ________________

漢字の練習 | Kanji practice

1 Trace the gray kanji first, then write each kanji twice as neatly as possible.

S=stop F=flick R=release C=curved line ↓ → =direction ◯=note ◌=space

292 覚 1 2 3 4 5 6 7 8 9 10 11 12 F
覚

293 貸 1 2 3 4 5 6 7 8 9 10 11 12 F Watch position
貸

294 借 1 2 3 4 5 6 7 8 9 10
借

295 待 1 2 3 4 5 6 7 8 9
待

296 落 1 2 3 4 5 6 7 8 9 10 11 12 R R
落

297 違 1 Cross 2 3 4 5 6 7 8 9 10 11 12 13
違

298 死 1 2 3 4 5 6
死

299 多 stacked vertically 1 2 3 4 5 6 bigger than above
多

300 少 1 2 3 4 F C Start here
少

301 工 1 2 3 short long
工

302 主 1 2 3 4 5 short long
主

303 員 1 2 3 4 5 6 7 8 9 10
員

Class: ___________ Name: ___________________________

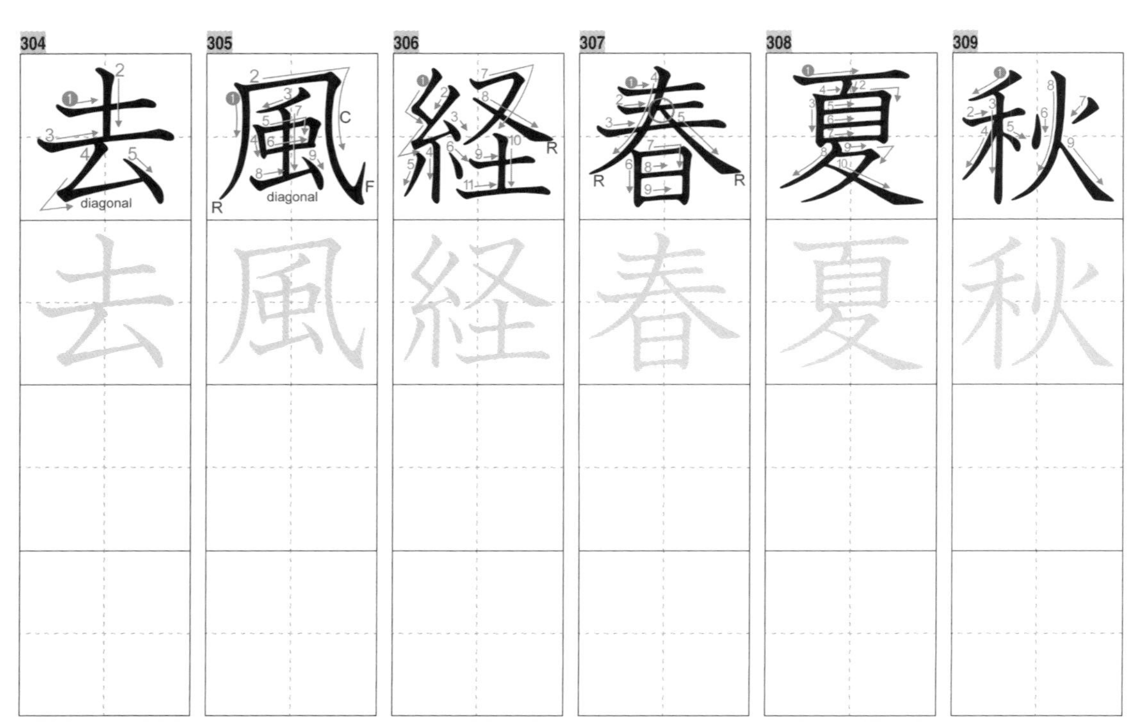

310
冬
Slant downward

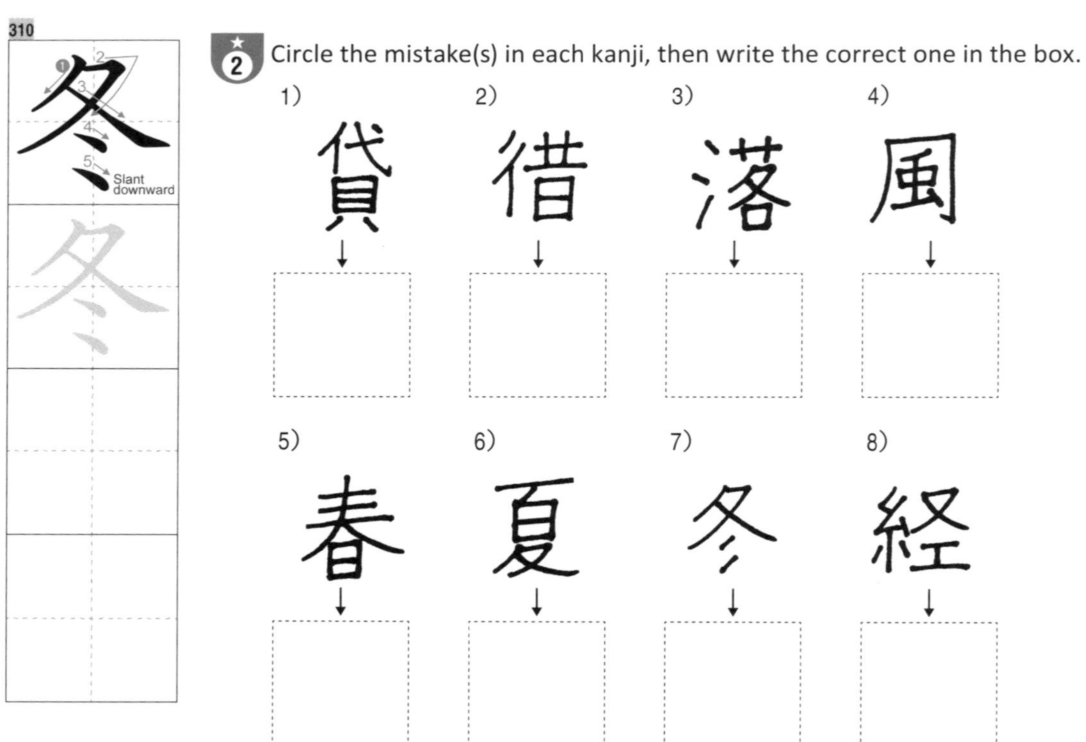

Class: __________ Name: ______________________

3 Identify the hidden parts of each kanji and rewrite that kanji in the box below. Then, provide its reading vertically in ( ).

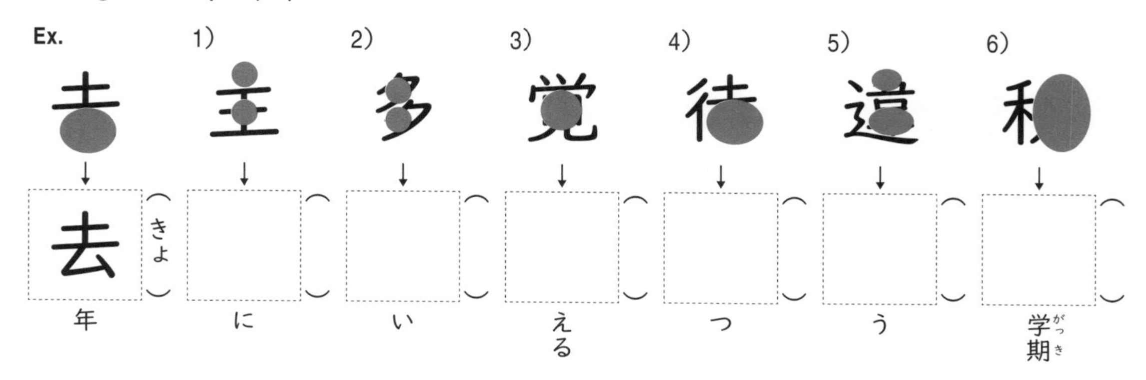

年　に　い　える　つ　う　学期(がっき)

4 Choose the correct combination of kanji and its *okurigana*.

1) その落語の話を [a. 少こし　b. 少し] [a. 覚ぼえて　b. 覚えて　c. 覚て] いる。

2) 大学の近くに部屋を [a. 借りる　b. 借る] つもりだ。

3) 大変だ！どこかでクレジットカードを [a. 落として　b. 落して　c. 落て] しまったみたいだ。

4) このジムを利用している人は会社員が [a. 多おくて　b. 多くて　c. 多て]、学生は [a. 少くない　b. 少ない　c. 少い]。

5) ウェブサイトで [a. 調らべた　b. 調べた　c. 調た] 住所が [a. 違がって　b. 違って　c. 違て] いて、郵便(ゆうびん)が戻(もど)ってきてしまった。

5 Provide the readings for the kanji words and compounds in __. Then, categorize their corresponding letters into the given groups.

a. 多い __________　b. 主に __________　c. 会社員 __________　d. 会場 __________

e. 夏 __________　f. 秋 __________　g. 工場 __________　h. 去年 __________

i. 少ない __________　j. 風 __________　k. 春 __________　l. 冬 __________

m. 間違い __________　n. 落語家 __________

季節(きせつ)	自然(しぜん) (nature)	場所	職業(しょくぎょう) (occupation)	形容詞(けいようし)	その他(ほか) (other)

Lesson 19

Class: __________ Name: ____________________

6 For each picture, fill in __ with the corresponding word using kanji from this lesson. Use the dictionary form and add *okurigana* as necessary.

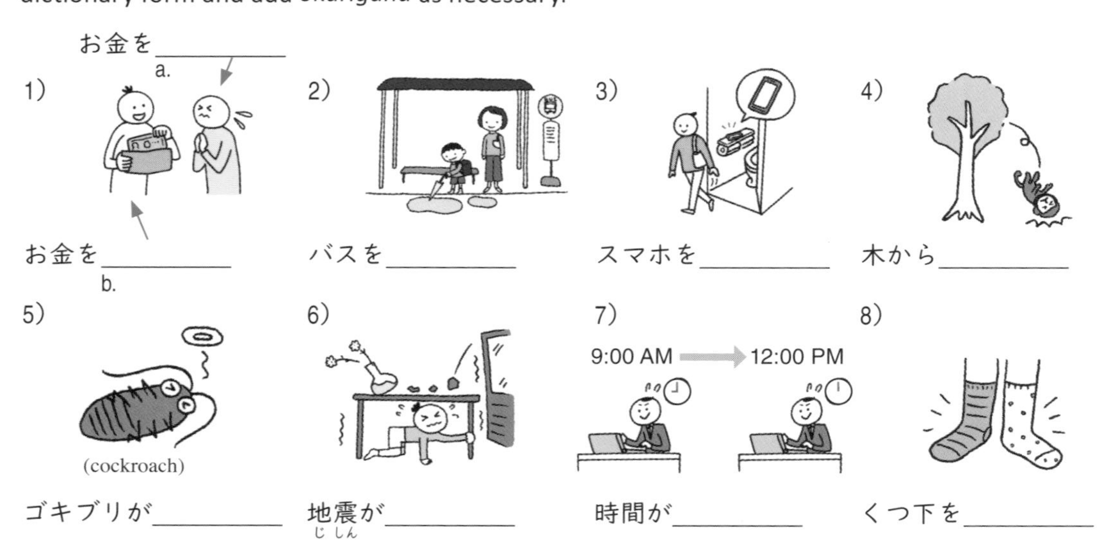

1) a. お金を______ b. お金を______

2) バスを______

3) スマホを______

4) 木から______

5) ゴキブリが______

6) 地震(じしん)が______

7) 時間が______

8) くつ下を______

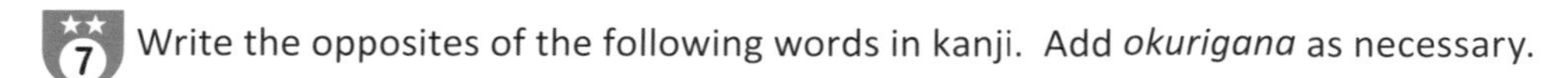

7 Write the opposites of the following words in kanji. Add *okurigana* as necessary.

1) 貸す ↔ ______

2) 忘れる ↔ ______ [not 思い出す]

3) 拾う ↔ ______

4) 電話をかける ↔ 電話を______

5) 生きる ↔ ______

6) 同じ ↔ ______

7) 少ない ↔ ______

8) 正しい ↔ ______

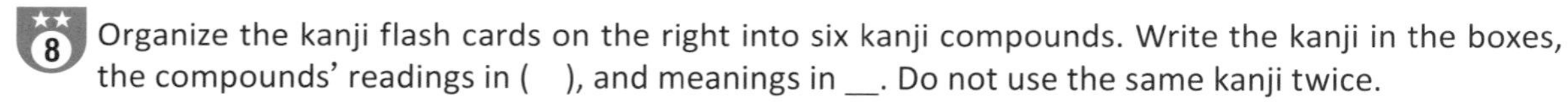

8 Organize the kanji flash cards on the right into six kanji compounds. Write the kanji in the boxes, the compounds' readings in ( ), and meanings in __. Do not use the same kanji twice.

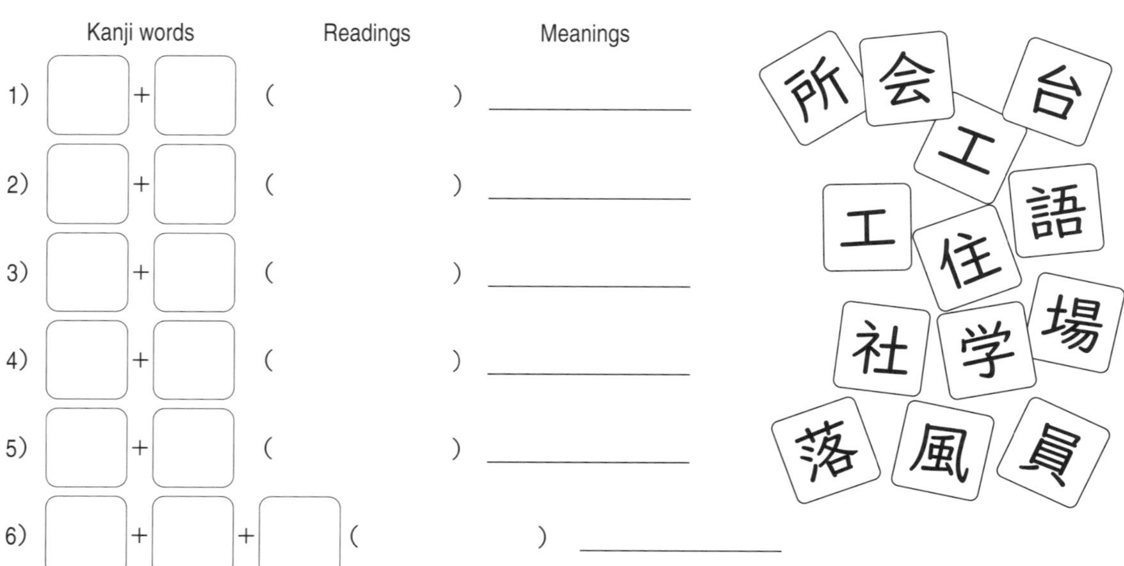

Kanji words	Readings	Meanings
1) □ + □	( )	______
2) □ + □	( )	______
3) □ + □	( )	______
4) □ + □	( )	______
5) □ + □	( )	______
6) □ + □ + □	( )	______

Class: ＿＿＿＿＿＿　Name: ＿＿＿＿＿＿＿＿＿＿＿＿

★★ 9 The underlined kanji below are incorrect. Provide the correct kanji given the context as in the example.

Ex. 時間が立つ
Ex. 経

1）空港で友達を持つ

2）ジムを私用する

3）大風が来る

4）コンサートの回場

5）名前と主所

6）人が小ない

7）宿題が大い

8）日本の会社買

9）ビールの工所

10）間近いやすい敬語（けいご）

11）図書官（a.）で本を貸（b.）りる

★★ 10 Fill in each red box to make two kanji compounds, then provide the reading for each compound in (　). Based on the meanings of those compounds, deduce the meaning of their shared kanji and write it in ＿.

Ex.

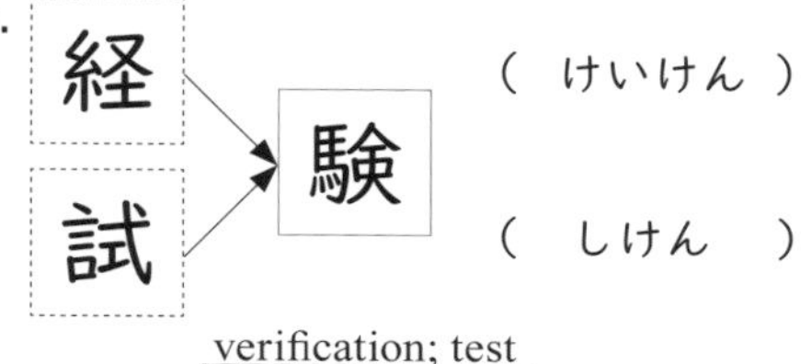

verification; test

1）

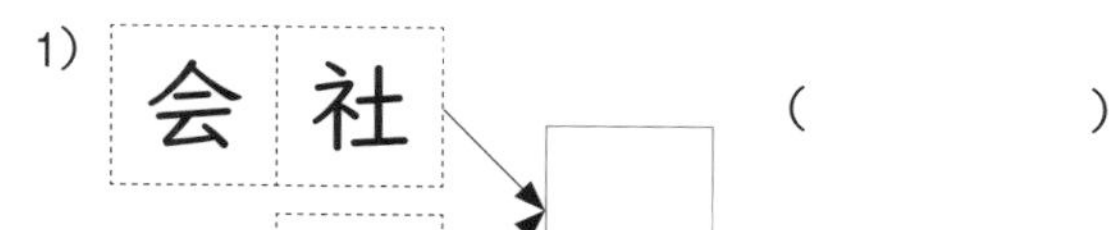

＿＿＿＿

2）

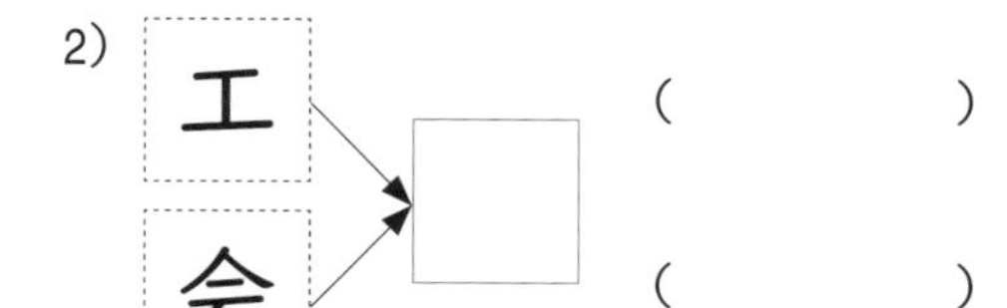

＿＿＿＿

3）

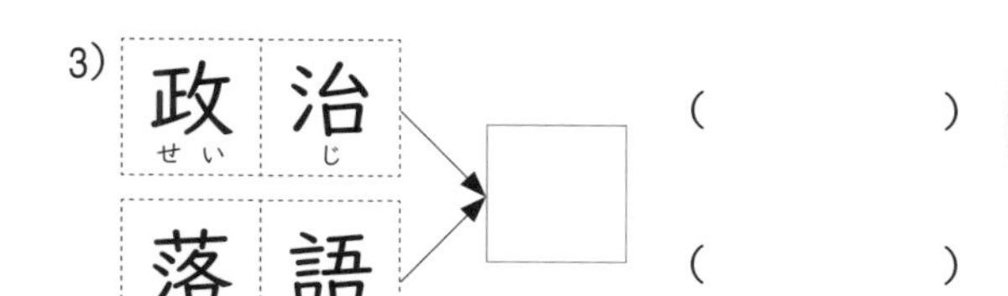

＿＿＿＿

4）

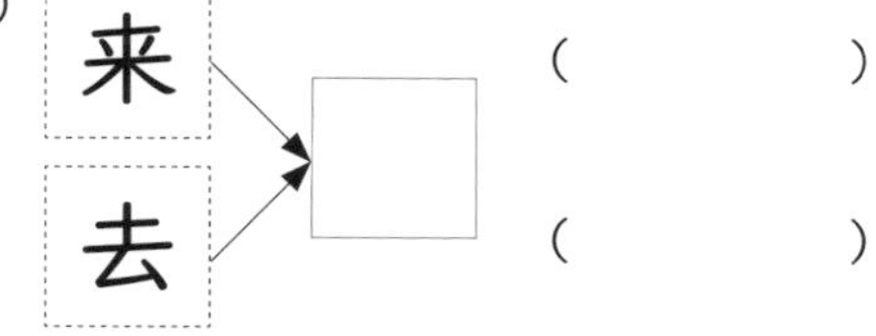

＿＿＿＿

5）

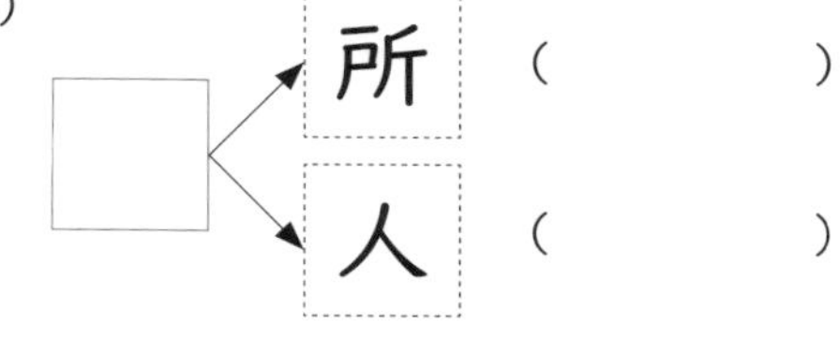

＿＿＿＿

Lesson 19

Class: __________ Name: ______________________

11 Provide the readings for words 1)-7) in ( ), then match each word with its explanation on the right.

1) (家に)上がる (　　　　　　)・　　・物や場所やサービスを使うこと
2) 利用する (　　　　　　)・　　・忘れていた物やことが思い浮(う)かぶ (to come to mind) こと
3) 違う (　　　　　　)・　　・日本の家の中に入ること
4) 思い出す (　　　　　　)・　　・たくさん
5) 主に (　　　　　　)・　　・同じじゃないこと
6) 多く (　　　　　　)・　　・ちょっと
7) 少し (　　　　　　)・　　・たいていの場合(ばあい) (in most cases); 多くの部分(ぶぶん) (part)

12 Provide the kanji for the underlined hiragana words. Add *okurigana* and other hiragana as necessary. The numbers in ( ) indicate the total number of kanji that should be provided.

1) 今年のなつ(a.)は暑(あつ)くて、たいふう(b.)がおおい(c.)。私がいる所はかぜ(d.)がつよい(e.)と停電(ていでん)しやすいので、たいへん(f.)だ。(8)

2) きのう(a.)がんばってかんじ(b.)をおぼえた(c.)のに、小テストの時にすこし(d.) まちがえて(e.)しまった。(8)

3) きょねん(a.)のふゆやすみ(b.)にかいしゃいん(c.)の兄と一緒(いっしょ)に日本に遊(あそ)びに行った。その時、一週間だけかりられる(d.) へや(e.)をりよう(f.)した。(12)

4) こうがく(a.)のじゅぎょう(b.)でくるま(c.)のこうじょう(d.)を見に行った。そこではおもに(e.)ロボットがくるまを作っていて、はたらいて(f.)いる人はすくなかった(g.)。(10)

5) 友達にかして(a.)もらった本をおとして(b.) よごして(c.)しまったから、謝(あやま)らなくてはいけない。(3)

6) しにそうな(a.)けがをして手術(しゅじゅつ)をうけた(b.)。おもいだす(c.)と、ほんとう(d.)にこわいけいけん(e.)だった。(8)

7) 今日、母とイベントのかいじょう(a.)で会う約束(やくそく)をしたけれど、母はちがう(b.) ばしょ(c.)でまって(d.)いた。でも、会えたからよかった。(6)

Class: ___________ Name: ___________________________

13 (★★) Provide the readings for the kanji of the underlined words.

インターンシップの会社で自己紹介(じこしょうかい)をする

初め(a.)まして。スカイ・ウィンターと申(もう)します。日本語を勉強しているので、日本で生活(b.)してみたくて、こちらの仕事に応募(おうぼ)しました (to apply)。専攻(せんこう)は工学(c.)で、主に(d.)プログラミングの勉強をしております。名前はウィンターで冬(e.)ですが、好きな季節(きせつ)は夏(f.)で、好きな食べ物はかき氷(ごおり)です。去年(g.)から落語(h.)に興味(きょうみ)を持っていて、週末(i.)を利用(j.)してよく落語を聞きに行きます。

得意(とくい)なことは人とすぐに仲良(なかよ)くなることです。でも、人の名前を覚える(k.)のはちょっと苦手(にがて)で、時々間違えたり(l.)思い出せ(m.)なかったりします。色々な(n.)ことを学んで(o.)、できるだけ多く(p.)、いい経験(q.)をしたいと思っています。どうぞよろしくお願(ねが)いいたします。

14 (★★★) Using #13 as a model, write a short self-introduction (for school, work, social media profile, etc.). Use kanji that you have learned in LL3-19 as much as possible.

Lesson 19

Class: ____________　Name: ______________________

読む練習 | Reading practice

▶『とびらII』L19「小話」(p.348) と「落語」(p.349) を読んで、答えなさい。

中級(ちゅうきゅう) (intermediate) に行くための準備(じゅんび)　4つのステップで読んでみよう

Step 1

まず、自分で読む。

Step 2

次に、「とびら初級WEBサイト」の音声(おんせい) (audio recordings) を聞く。

Step 3

それから、音声(おんせい)を聞きながら漢字の読み方をチェックする。

Step 4

最後に、音声(おんせい)と一緒(いっしょ)に読んでみる。

読み物を読もう

読み物1　**小話(こばなし)**（p.348）（短(みじか)くてちょっとおもしろい話）

1）どの話が一番おもしろいと思いましたか。なぜそう思いましたか。

2）小話(こばなし)を一つ選(えら)んで、～～の部分(ぶぶん)を他の言葉(ことば)に変えて、パロディを作ってみましょう。

〈例〉選(えら)んだ小話(こばなし)［ 1 ］テストで100点を取らせてください。

→ サッカーの試合でゴールをさせてください。

選(えら)んだ小話(こばなし)［　］______________________________

読み物2　**『まんじゅうこわい』**（p.349）（落語の有名な話）

1 あなたがこわいと思うものは何ですか。どうしてそれがこわいですか。

____

2 日本語のオノマトペについて考えてみましょう。

1）下の表(ひょう)の①～④のオノマトペが『まんじゅうこわい』のどこにあるか見つけて、行数(ぎょうすう) (line number) を入れなさい。

2）①～④のオノマトペのタイプに○をしなさい。

Type1：Mimics sounds of people, animals, objects, and natural phenomena

Type2：Represents both physical and psychological states as well as manners of action

3）どんな時に使われると思いますか。A.～D. の中から選(えら)びなさい。

A. おいしそうにたくさん食べる　B. 何も言わないでいっしょうけんめい食べる

C. 気持ちが悪い　D. 地震(じしん)で地面(じめん) (ground) や色々なものがゆれる

	オノマトペ	行数(ぎょうすう)	オノマトペのタイプ	どんな時に使われるか
①	ぐらぐら		Type 1　Type 2	A　B　C　D
②	オェ／オェ～		Type 1　Type 2	A　B　C　D
③	もぐもぐ		Type 1　Type 2	A　B　C　D
④	パクパク		Type 1　Type 2	A　B　C　D

Class: ________ Name: ____________________

3 『まんじゅうこわい』の話を読んで、質問に答えなさい。

1) 20行目(ぎょうめ)：マツの答えを読む前に、マツのこわいものは何だと思いましたか。

____

2) 37行目(ぎょうめ)：「そう言うと」の「そう」は文のどこからどこまでを指(さ)していますか。最初と最後の言葉(ことば)を書きなさい。

______________________から______________________まで

3) 42行目(ぎょうめ)から44行目(ぎょうめ)：みんながマツのそばにまんじゅうを置(お)いた後で、どんなことが起こると思いましたか。

____

4) 54行目(ぎょうめ)から55行目(ぎょうめ)：「それを見て」の「それ」は文のどこからどこまでを指(さ)していますか。最初と最後の言葉(ことば)を書きなさい。

______________________から______________________まで

4 スピーチスタイルについて考えてみましょう。

1) マツはみんなとどんなスピーチスタイルで話していますか。

____

2) そのことから何が分かりますか。

____

Lesson 19

5 話の順番(じゅんばん)に（　　）に番号(ばんごう)を入れなさい。

A.（　　）　B.（　　）　C.（　　）

D.（　　）　E.（　　）　F.（　　）

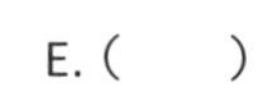

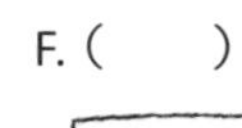

Class: ____________ Name: ____________________________

書く練習 | Writing practice

▶書くシートは「とびら初級WEBサイト」にあります。

『まんじゅうこわい』のパロディを書く

タスク：あなたの「○○こわい」という話を作ってみましょう。「こわいもの」は食べ物・飲み物、着る物、人、趣味、場所、何でもいいです。おもしろいパロディを作ってください。

1 **書く前に**：下の『まんじゅうこわい』のアウトラインを見て、自分の話のアウトラインを考えなさい。

■『まんじゅうこわい』のアウトライン

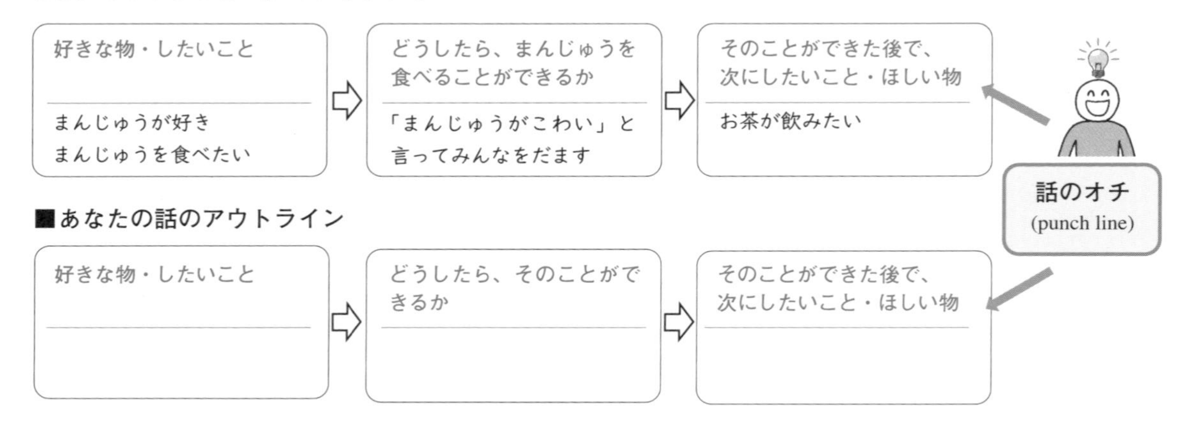

2 **書く**：上のアウトラインをもとに (based on) して、自分の「○○こわい」の話を書きなさい。（「とびら初級WEBサイト」にある書くシートのテンプレートを使ってもいいです）

Checklist

✓	オリジナリティがある話を書く。
✓	です・ますフォームで書く。
✓	習った漢字をできるだけたくさん使う。
✓	下の文法をできるだけたくさん使う。

- ☐ Casual speech style (for conversation)
- ☐ Noun modification clauses
- ☐ Passive forms
- ☐ Causative forms
- ☐ V-*te* (causative) {あげる／くれる／もらう}
- ☐ Causative-passive forms
- ☐ ～か(どうか) [Embedded question]
- ☐ ～と [Conditional]

3 **書いた後で**：自分の「○○こわい」の話をみんなの前で話しなさい。（時間がなかったら、「書く前に」で考えたアウトラインを紹介してもいいです）

Exit Check

Now go back to the Kanji List for this lesson (p.88) and do the exit check to see what kanji you can read and write.

Class: ＿＿＿＿＿＿　Name: ＿＿＿＿＿＿＿＿＿＿＿＿

漢字の復習(3)｜Kanji Review (3) [Lessons 17-19]

17課から19課で新しく習った漢字の復習をしましょう。全部読んだり書いたりできますか。読み方や書き方が分からない漢字には○をして、よく復習しましょう。

The highlighted kanji words include new readings for kanji you've already learned.

Nouns	<もの> 授業料　写真　顔　地図　図　大学院　地球　台風　風 <こと> 試合　野球　空手　生活　活動　授業　留守　用事　落語 <人> 教授　人間　大学院生　留学生　野口さん　両親　落語家　会社員 <所> 北海道　研究室　病院　地下　地方　長野　空港　空　工場 会場　北　北口　南　南口　西　西口　東　東口 <時> 最近　(お)正月　去年　春　春休み　夏　夏休み　秋　秋休み　冬　冬休み <その他(other)> 考え　答え　間違い　分野　工学　住所
Verbs	(～を)落とす　送る　学ぶ　残す　広げる　覚える　待つ　間違える　卒業する 経験する｜(～を／について)考える　研究する｜(～に)近づく　通う　答える 間に合う　留学する｜(家に)上がる　(病院に)入院する｜(～に～を)貸す　借りる｜ (～について)話し合う｜(～が)落ちる　経つ　集まる　起こる　歩く　急ぐ　生きる 死ぬ　残業する　安心する｜(～は～と／～と～は)違う
Adjs.	近い　正しい　重い　弱い　多い　少ない　幸せ(な)　便利(な)　不便(な)　楽(な)
Advs.	急に　少し　主に
Other	用事がある　他に　他のN　多くのN　少しのN

上の漢字をできるだけたくさん使って、「学ぶ」の漢字マップを作ってみましょう。

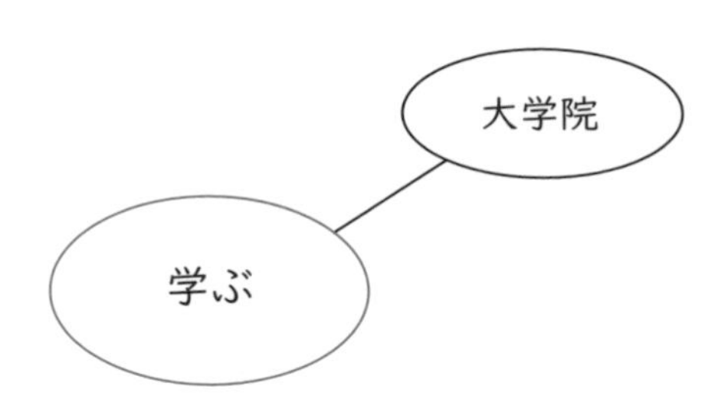

Lesson 20 みんな、これからどうするの？

What's everyone doing next?

Kanji List できるCheck ✓

	311	312	313	314	315	316	317	318	319	320	321	322	323	324	325	326	327	328	329
Kanji	結	婚	果	予	約	定	全	伝	感	暑	寒	犬	赤	青	白	黒	銀	紙	葉
Entry Check																			
Exit Check																			

Kanji elements Below are kanji introduced up to L20, sorted by elements they have in common. Those in bold are new kanji introduced in this lesson.

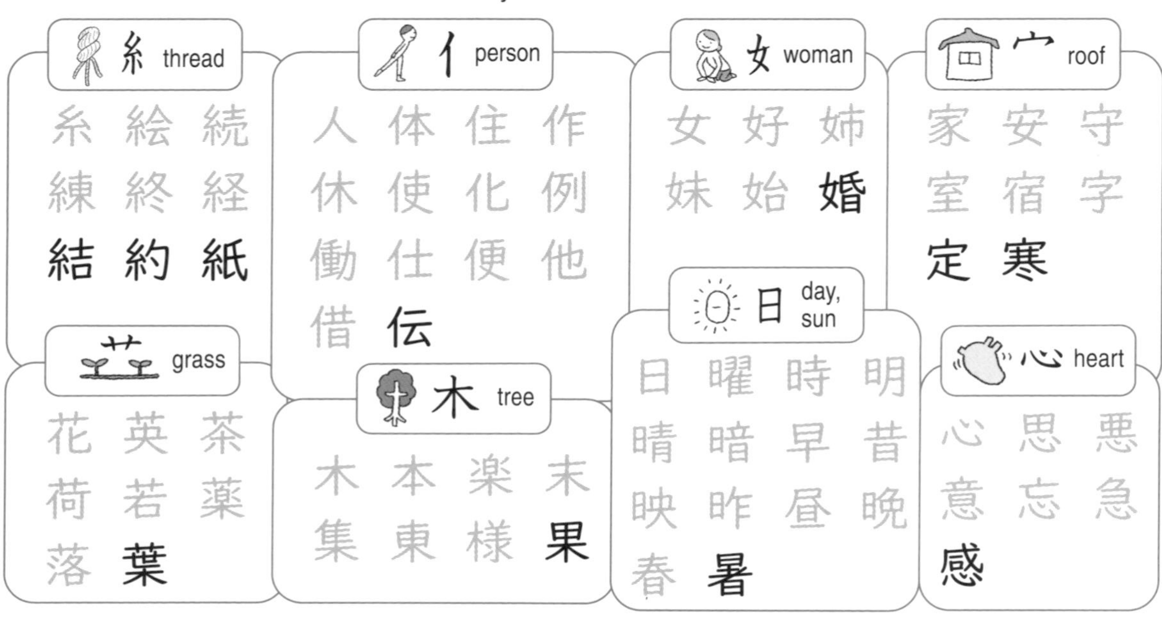

Kanji in daily life Which kanji can you recognize?

Class: __________ Name: ____________________

漢字の練習 | Kanji practice

1 Trace the gray kanji first, then write each kanji twice as neatly as possible.

S=stop F=flick R=release C=curved line ↓ → =direction ◯=note ◌=space

311 結 (long, short)

312 婚

313 果 (one stroke)

314 予 (touching, F)

315 約 (F)

316 定

317 全 (Don't cross)

318 伝 (short, long, one stroke)

319 感 (F, F)

320 暑 (Start here)

321 寒 (Slant downward)

322 犬

Lesson 20

Class: ___________ Name: ___________________________

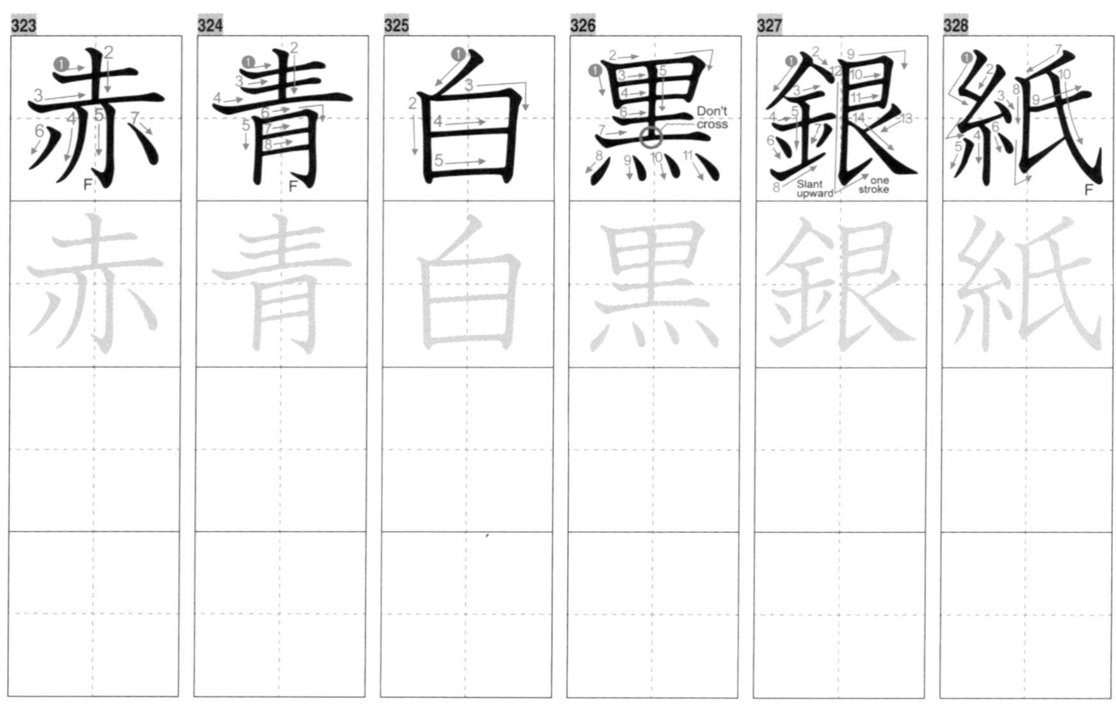

2 Circle the mistake(s) in each kanji, then write the correct one in the box.

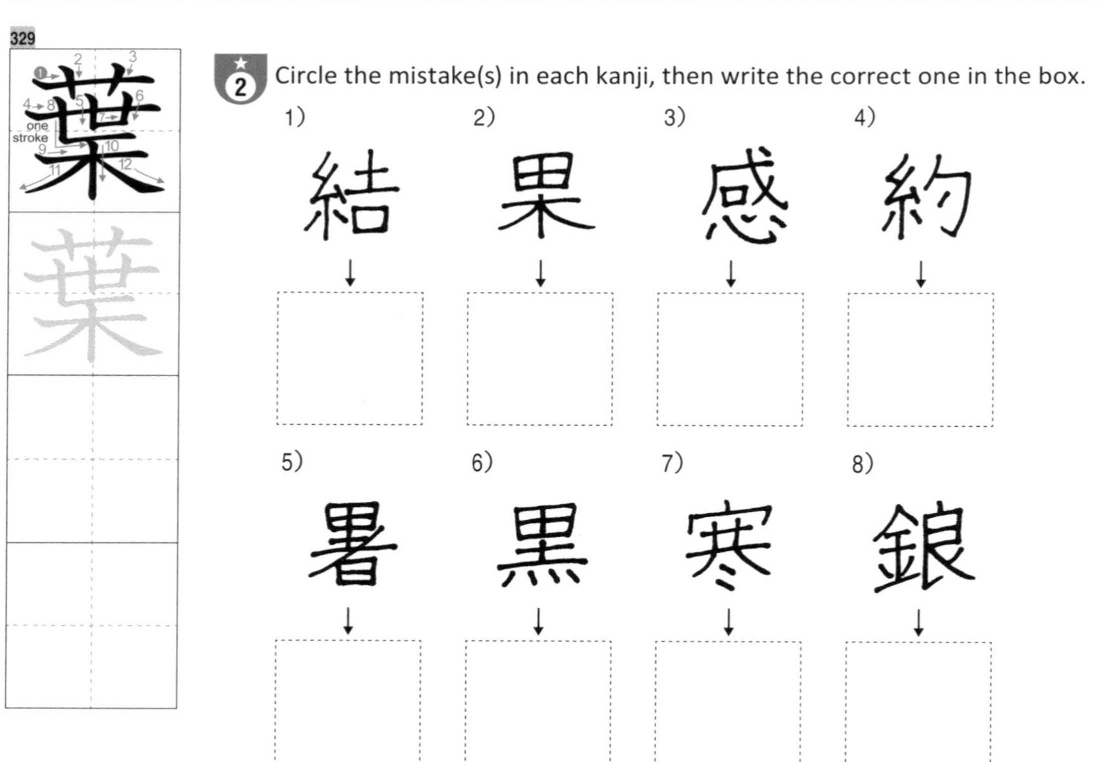

Class: ___________ Name: ________________________

3 Complete kanji and kanji compounds 1)-8) by adding an element from the box below. Then, provide the reading for eachss word in ( ) and its meanings in __. You may use the same element more than once.

4 For each picture, write the corresponding kanji or kanji compound in __, then provide its reading in ( ).

1) ____________ ( )

2) ____________ ( ) SCHEDULE

3) ____________ ( ) result 1. 2. 3.

4) ____________ ( ) BANK

5) ____________ ( )

6) ____________る ( )

7) ____________ ( )

8) ____________ ( )

9) ____________く ( ) To Be Continued

5 This time, you spilled coffee over your kanji flash cards! Rewrite the words on the flash cards, then provide their readings in ( ) and meanings in __.

Kanji words	Readings	Meanings
Ex. 予習	(よしゅう)	preparatory study
1) ________	( )	________
2) ________	( )	________
3) ________	( )	________
4) ________	( )	________
5) ________	( )	________
6) ________	( )	________
7) ________	( )	________

Ex. 予習 1) 手伝う 2) 言葉 3) 安全な 4) 感動する 5) 手紙 6) 大人 7) 犬

Lesson 20

Class: ＿＿＿＿＿　Name: ＿＿＿＿＿＿＿＿＿＿

6 Make kanji by combining one element each from A (top element) and B (bottom element). Then, insert the appropriate kanji in the boxes to complete the words and phrases in 1)-6). Provide their readings in (　).

A: 人　土　艹　耂　丶　丿

B: 日　月　王　小　業　大

1) ☐い雪 (　　)

2) ☐い海 (　　)

3) ☐っぱ (　　)

4) ☐ちゃん (　　)

5) ☐部で (　　)

6) ペットの☐ (　　)

7 Choose the most appropriate kanji to complete each sentence.

1) この建物(たてもの)はエレベーターがなくて、不［a. 便　b. 使　c. 更］ですね。

2) A：［a. 全　b. 金］部で15,000円です。

B：えっ、15,000円？　日本は［a. 東　b. 果　c. 車］物が高いですね。

3) 私の［a. 犬　b. 木　c. 大］はとても頭(あたま)がいいです。

4) 赤いシャツと一緒(いっしょ)にせんたくしたら、［a. 百　b. 自　c. 白］いシャツがピンクになってしまった。

5) 結婚式(しき) (ceremony) に［a. 里　b. 黒　c. 果］いネクタイをして行ってもいいですか。

6) この仕事を手［a. 伝　b. 云　c. 仕］ってもらえませんか。

7) ［a. 着　b. 者　c. 暑］いから、海に泳(およ)ぎに行った。

8 Provide the readings for the kanji words in ＿. Then, categorize their corresponding letters into the given groups.

a. 気にする ＿＿＿＿	b. 感じる ＿＿＿＿	c. 寒い ＿＿＿＿
d. 伝える ＿＿＿＿	e. 青い ＿＿＿＿	f. 鳥 ＿＿＿＿
g. 牛 ＿＿＿＿	h. くり返す ＿＿＿＿	i. 黒い ＿＿＿＿
j. 赤い ＿＿＿＿	k. 犬 ＿＿＿＿	l. 暑い ＿＿＿＿

動物	色	気候(きこう) (climate)	動詞(どうし)

Class: ＿＿＿＿＿ Name: ＿＿＿＿＿＿＿＿＿＿

9 Write the opposites of the following words in kanji. Then, provide their readings in ( ). Add *okurigana* as necessary.

1) 白 ↔ ＿＿＿＿＿ (　　　　　)

2) 危険(きけん)(な) ↔ ＿＿＿＿＿ (　　　　　)

SAFE ZONE

3) 離婚(りこん)する ↔ ＿＿＿＿＿ (　　　　　)

4) 暑い ↔ ＿＿＿＿＿ (　　　　　)

5) 復習(ふくしゅう)する ↔ ＿＿＿＿＿ (　　　　　)

(after class)　(before class)

6) 子ども ↔ ＿＿＿＿＿ (　　　　　)

7) かぎをかける ↔ ＿＿＿＿＿ (　　　　　)

8) 青 ↔ ＿＿＿＿＿ (　　　　　)

(sky)

10 Fill in each ＿ with the appropriate word from the box. Use kanji where applicable as in the example.

ことば　　くうき　　つたえて　　まわって　　かんどうして　　てつだって

Ex. チェンさん、すみませんが、先生に授業に遅れると＿伝えて＿ください。

1) 先週末、とてもいい映画を見て、＿＿＿＿＿＿、泣いてしまった。

2) 昨日、弟の宿題を＿＿＿＿＿＿あげた。

3) 自転車のタイヤに＿＿＿＿＿＿を入れなくてはいけない。

4) ＿＿＿＿＿＿を勉強すると、その国の文化が分かります。

5) 地球は自転(じてん) (rotation) しています。１回24時間ぐらいで＿＿＿＿＿いいます。

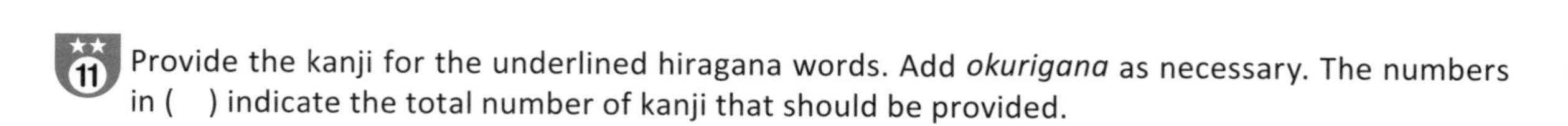

11 Provide the kanji for the underlined hiragana words. Add *okurigana* as necessary. The numbers in ( ) indicate the total number of kanji that should be provided.

1) くろだ(a.)先生、日本ではかぞく(b.)のけっこん(c.)式(しき) (ceremony) に、男の人はくろい(d.)スーツをきて(e.)、しろい(f.)ネクタイをしていく人が多いそうですが、本当ですか。(9)

2) A：しけん(a.)、どうだった？　ぜんぶ(b.)できた？

B：ううん、はんぶん(c.)ぐらいこたえられなかった(d.)。けっか(e.)は知りたくない。(9)

Class: __________ Name: ______________________

3) 小さい時、そらはどうしてあおいか、ゆうがたになるとどうしてあかくなるか、りょうしん
a. b. c. d. e.

に聞いてみた。(7)

4) A：こんしゅうまつ、何もよていがなかったら、えいがを見に行かない？
a. b. c.

B：いいね。かんどうするのが見たいな。
d.

A：あ、いいね。じゃあ、よさそうなのをしらべて、チケットをよやくしておこうか。
e. f.

B：うん、お願い(ねが)。えいがかんはさむいから、ジャケットを持っていったほうがいいね。(17)
g. h. i.

5) 人といい関係(かんけい)を作るために、気持ちはことばでつたえることがだいじだ。たとえば、感謝(かんしゃ)の
a. b. c. d.

気持ちやかんじていることをてがみやカードでつたえたら、よろこんで
e. f.

もらえるだろう。(9)

12 (★★) Below is an essay from a student describing his semester using the kanji 寒. Provide the readings for the kanji of the underlined words.(Refer to #2 on p.388 of *TOBIRA II*.)

私の今学期(こんがっき)の漢字

私の今学期(こんがっき)の漢字は「寒」です。今年の冬、カナダから初めて京都(きょうと)に来たんですが、とて
a. b. c. d. e.

も寒く感じたからです。カナダでは家の中を全部暖(あたた)めますが、日本では人がいる部屋しか
f. g. h. i. j. k. l.

暖(あたた)めません。例えば、人がいないお風呂(ふろ)やお手洗いは暖(あたた)かくないです。だから、お手洗い
m. n.

に行く時は寒くていやでしたが、誰(だれ)もいない所にエネルギーを使わなくてもいいし、地球に
o. p. q.

やさしいと思いました。
r.

13 (★★★) Using #12 as a model, write about a kanji that you feel best describes your semester or year. Use kanji that you have learned in LL3-20 as much as possible.

Class: ＿＿＿＿＿　Name: ＿＿＿＿＿＿＿＿＿＿

読む練習 | Reading practice

▶『とびら II』L20 読みましょう (pp.382-386) を読んで、答えなさい。

読み物を読む前に

1 次の質問に日本語で答えなさい。日本語で言えないタイトルやフレーズは日本語じゃなくてもいいです。

詩(し)を読んだことがありますか。　[はい・いいえ]

- 「はい」の人：詩(し)のタイトル＿＿＿＿＿＿＿＿

  作者＿＿＿＿＿＿＿＿　何語(なにご)？＿＿＿＿＿＿＿＿

  その詩(し)の中の好きなフレーズや覚えている言葉があったら書きなさい。

  ＿＿＿＿＿＿＿＿＿＿＿＿＿＿＿＿

- 「いいえ」の人：歌詞(かし)が好きな歌がありますか。

  歌のタイトル＿＿＿＿＿＿＿＿

  歌手＿＿＿＿＿＿＿＿　何語(なにご)？＿＿＿＿＿＿＿＿

  その歌詞(かし)の中の好きなフレーズや言葉があったら書きなさい。

  ＿＿＿＿＿＿＿＿＿＿＿＿＿＿＿＿

2 音とリズムを楽しむ

1)『ことばあそびうた』(p.382) の詩(し)の中で、どの言葉がくり返されていますか。その言葉を書きなさい。

2) この二つの詩(し)を読んで、どう思いましたか。

＿＿＿＿＿＿＿＿＿＿＿＿＿＿＿＿

3 メタファーを考える

あなたの言葉では、下の色や言葉にはどんな意味がありますか。何をイメージしますか。その言葉を一つか二つ書きなさい。

赤		青		黒	
鳥		山		雪	

Class: __________ Name: ______________________

詩を読んでみよう

1 『こだまでしょうか』(p.383)という詩(し)を読んで、質問に答えなさい。

1)「こだま」は何だと思いますか。誰(だれ)と誰(だれ)が話していると思いますか。

2)「さみしくなって」というフレーズがありますが、さびしくなるのは誰(だれ)でしょうか。

3) 最後の行(ぎょう)の「いいえ、誰(だれ)でも」の後には、どんな言葉が続くと思いますか。

2 『生きる』(p.385)という詩(し)を読んで、質問に答えなさい。

1) あなたは「生きる」という言葉にどんなイメージを持ちますか。どんな言葉を連想(れんそう) (to associate) しますか。マインドマップ(p.384)をできるだけ日本語で作ってみましょう。

2)『生きる』を声(こえ)に出(だ)さないで読んでみてください。

① この詩(し)の中にマインドマップに書いたのと同じ言葉があったら、下に書きなさい。

____

②「生きる」の英語の意味には to live; to be alive; to exist; to survive; to subsist など (and so on) がありますが、この詩(し)にはどの意味が合(あ)う (to fit) と思いますか。(自分が考える「生きる」の意味を書いてもいいです)

③ この詩(し)のどの言葉やフレーズが好きですか。

3)『生きる』には連(れん) (stanza) が五つあります。次の質問に答えなさい。

① それぞれの (each) 連(れん)のトピックは下の a.～ f. のどれか考えて、(　)にアルファベットを入れなさい。一つじゃなくてもいいです。

1番目の連(れん)(　　　　) 2番目の連(れん)(　　　　) 3番目の連(れん)(　　　　)
4番目の連(れん)(　　　　) 5番目の連(れん)(　　　　)

a. 今、生(い)き物(もの)がしていること	b. 気持ちや感情(かんじょう) (emotions)	c. 美(うつく)しいと思うもの
d. 体で感じたりすること	e. 今、地球で起こっていること	f. その他(ほか):__________

② それぞれの連(れん)はどんな読み方がいいと思いますか。(　)にアルファベットを入れなさい。一つじゃなくてもいいです。

1番目の連(れん)(　　　　) 2番目の連(れん)(　　　　) 3番目の連(れん)(　　　　)
4番目の連(れん)(　　　　) 5番目の連(れん)(　　　　)

a. 強く読む	b. やさしく読む	c. うれしそうに読む	d. 悲(かな)しそうに読む
e. 静(しず)かにゆっくり読む	f. 速(はや)く元気に読む	g. その他(ほか):______________	

Class: ________ Name: ________________

書く練習｜Writing practice

▶書くシートは「とびら初級WEBサイト」にあります。

自分の「生きる」という詩を書く

タスク：あなたの『生きる』という詩を作ってみましょう。

1 **書く前に**：下の表に3つの連 (stanza) のトピックとキーワードを書きなさい。マインドマップ(p.384)に書いた言葉を参考にする (to refer) と考えやすいです。

1つ目の連のトピック ________	キーワード： キーワードを使って作れるフレーズ：
2つ目の連のトピック ________	キーワード：(あなたならカタカナの言葉(10行目～14行目)の代わりに (instead of) どんな言葉を入れますか。カタカナ・漢字・ひらがなのどれでもいいですが、自分の言葉を考えなさい。) キーワードを使って作れるフレーズ：
3つ目の連のトピック ________	キーワード： キーワードを使って作れるフレーズ：

2 **書く**：上の表をもとに (based on) して、自分の「生きる」という詩を書きなさい。(「とびら初級WEBサイト」にある書くシートのテンプレートを使ってもいいです)

Checklist

✓	plain フォームで書く。(例：生きる、うれしい、いのちだ)
✓	オリジナリティがある詩を書く。
✓	習った言葉や漢字をできるだけたくさん使う。

3 **書いた後で**：自分の「生きる」の詩をみんなの前で読みなさい。(詩を全部読む時間がなかったら、一番いいと思う連を一つ紹介しなさい)

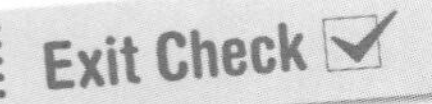

Now go back to the Kanji List for this lesson (p.100) and do the exit check to see what kanji you can read and write.

漢字リスト • Kanji List 『とびらI』

Lesson										
L3	1 一	2 二	3 三	4 四	5 五	6 六	7 七	8 八	9 九	10 十
	11 月	12 私	13 子	14 人						
L4	15 百	16 千	17 万	18 円	19 曜	20 日	21 火	22 水	23 木	24 金
	25 土	26 学	27 生	28 先	29 年	30 大	31 小			
L5	32 上	33 下	34 中	35 外	36 右	37 左	38 山	39 川	40 寺	41 何
	42 時	43 間	44 毎	45 明	46 今	47 田	48 町	49 花		
L6	50 食	51 飲	52 言	53 話	54 行	55 来	56 見	57 持	58 本	59 語
	60 体	61 口	62 目	63 耳	64 手	65 足	66 週	67 回		
L7	68 会	69 聞	70 読	71 立	72 住	73 知	74 入	75 売	76 買	77 物
	78 音	79 楽	80 海	81 国	82 門(E1)	83 矢(E2)	84 貝(E3)	85 牛(E4)		
L8	86 男	87 女	88 好	89 作	90 出	91 書	92 分	93 午	94 前	95 後
	96 有	97 名	98 父	99 母	100 兄	101 弟	102 姉	103 妹		
L9	104 思	105 休	106 悪	107 新	108 古	109 高	110 校	111 雨	112 雪	113 晴
	114 度	115 天	116 気	117 元	118 病	119 英	120 家	121 心(E5)		
L10	122 帰	123 使	124 暗	125 早	126 広	127 安	128 親	129 切	130 番	131 社
	132 長	133 道	134 昔	135 友	136 達	137 文	138 化	139 末		

* Kanji with "E" indicates the kanji used in many other kanji as elements, so you will encounter them frequently as you continue to study Japanese.

漢字リスト • Kanji List 『とびらⅡ』

L11	140	141	142	143	144	145	146	147	148	149
	勉	強	着	自	場	所	茶	料	理	肉
	150	151	152	153	154	155	156	157	158	
	鳥	魚	絵	例	方	次	最	王 (E6)	糸 (E7)	
L12	159	160	161	162	163	164	165	166	167	168
	集	配	動	働	走	当	荷	由	計	画
	169	170	171	172	173	174	175	176	177	
	映	仕	事	初	東	京	同	半	士 (E8)	
L13	178	179	180	181	182	183	184	185	186	187
	拾	返	守	変	止	電	車	神	様	注
	188	189	190	191	192	193	194	195	196	
	意	味	色	々	世	界	記	昨	若	
L14	197	198	199	200	201	202	203	204	205	206
	開	閉	消	汚	乗	遅	困	運	転	痛
	207	208	209	210	211	212	213	214	215	
	医	者	薬	服	店	部	屋	教	室	
L15	216	217	218	219	220	221	222	223	224	225
	続	助	調	忘	図	館	質	問	宿	題
	226	227	228	229	230	231	232	233	234	
	試	験	受	練	習	飯	族	夕	馬 (E9)	
L16	235	236	237	238	239	240	241	242	243	244
	取	泣	笑	起	始	終	決	歌	洗	台
	245	246	247	248	249	250	251	252	253	
	旅	駅	朝	昼	晩	夜	漢	字	竹 (E10)	
L17	254	255	256	257	258	259	260	261	262	263
	北	南	西	合	送	活	近	歩	急	授
	264	265	266	267	268	269	270	271	272	
	卒	業	写	真	研	究	顔	幸	正	
L18	273	274	275	276	277	278	279	280	281	282
	院	通	考	答	残	留	重	便	利	不
	283	284	285	286	287	288	289	290	291	
	弱	用	地	球	野	空	港	両	他	
L19	292	293	294	295	296	297	298	299	300	301
	覚	貸	借	待	落	違	死	多	少	工
	302	303	304	305	306	307	308	309	310	
	主	員	去	風	経	春	夏	秋	冬	
L20	311	312	313	314	315	316	317	318	319	320
	結	婚	果	予	約	定	全	伝	感	暑
	321	322	323	324	325	326	327	328	329	
	寒	犬	赤	青	白	黒	銀	紙	葉	

著者紹介

岡 まゆみ • Mayumi Oka

現職　ミドルベリー日本語学校日本語大学院プログラム講師
教歴　ミシガン大学アジア言語文化学科日本語学課長
プリンストン大学専任講師，コロンビア大学専任講師，上智大学講師
著書　『中・上級者のための速読の日本語 第2版』（2013）;『マルチメディア日本語基本文法ワークブック』（共著）（2018）（以上、ジャパンタイムズ出版）;『上級へのとびら』（2009）;『きたえよう漢字力』（2010）;『中級日本語を教える教師の手引き』（2011）;『これで身につく文法力』（2012）;『日英共通メタファー辞典』（2017）;『初級日本語 とびらⅠ』（2021）;『初級日本語 とびらⅡ』（2022）;『とびらⅠワークブック 1』（2022）;『とびらⅠワークブック 2』（2023）（以上共著、くろしお出版）; その他
その他　全米日本語教師学会理事（2007-2010）
ミシガン大学 Matthews Underclass Teaching Award（2019）

近藤 純子 • Junko Kondo

現職　南山大学外国人留学生別科専任語学講師
教歴　マドンナ大学非常勤講師，ミシガン大学専任講師
著書　『上級へのとびら』（2009）;『きたえよう漢字力』（2010）;『中級日本語を教える教師の手引き』（2011）;『これで身につく文法力』（2012）;『初級日本語 とびらⅠ』（2021）;『初級日本語 とびらⅡ』（2022）;『とびらⅠワークブック 1』（2022）;『とびらⅠワークブック 2』（2023）（以上共著、くろしお出版）

榊原 芳美 • Yoshimi Sakakibara

現職　ミシガン大学アジア言語文化学科専任講師
教歴　ミシガン州立大学専任講師，北海道国際交流センター日本語日本文化講座夏期セミナー講師
著書　『マルチメディア日本語基本文法ワークブック』（2018）（共著、ジャパンタイムズ出版）;『初級日本語 とびらⅠ』（2021）;『初級日本語 とびらⅡ』（2022）;『とびらⅠワークブック 1』（2022）;『とびらⅠワークブック 2』（2023）（以上共著、くろしお出版）

西村 裕代 • Hiroyo Nishimura

現職　イェール大学東アジア言語文学部専任講師
教歴　オバリン大学講師，オハイオ大学講師，ヴァッサー大学日本語フェロー，オレゴン大学夏期講習講師，CET Academic Program 夏期講習講師
著書　『とびらⅠワークブック 1』（2022）;『とびらⅠワークブック 2』（2023）（以上共著、くろしお出版）

筒井 通雄 • Michio Tsutsui ［監修］

現職　ワシントン大学人間中心設計工学科名誉教授
教歴　コロンビア大学日本語教育夏期修士プログラム講師，ワシントン大学教授，マサチューセッツ工科大学助教授，カリフォルニア大学デービス校客員助教授
著書　『日本語基本文法辞典』（1986）;『日本語文法辞典〈中級編〉』（1995）;『日本語文法辞典〈上級編〉』（2008）;『マルチメディア日本語基本文法ワークブック』（2018）（以上共著、ジャパンタイムズ出版）;『上級へのとびら』（2009）;『きたえよう漢字力』（2010）;『中級日本語を教える教師の手引き』（2011）;『これで身につく文法力』（2012）;『初級日本語 とびらⅠ』（2021）;『初級日本語 とびらⅡ』（2022）;『とびらⅠワークブック 1』（2022）;『とびらⅠワークブック 2』（2023）（以上共著、くろしお出版）; その他
その他　全米日本語教師学会理事（1990-1993，2009-2012）

制作協力

■ 校正・英語校正

平川ワイター永子（Eiko Hirakawa Weyter）

現職 フリーランス日本語教師

教歴 ミシガン大学専任講師，パデュー大学専任講師

■ 英語翻訳・校正

Robin Griffin（ロビン・グリフィン）

■ イラスト

坂木浩子

村山宇希

■ 装丁・本文デザイン

鈴木章宏

■ 編集

市川麻里子

初級日本語 とびらII ワークブック 1
一漢字，読む，書く

TOBIRA II: Beginning Japanese Workbook 1
—Kanji, Reading, Writing

2023年 12月8日 第1刷発行

著　者 岡まゆみ・近藤純子・榊原芳美・西村裕代

監　修 筒井通雄

発行人 岡野秀夫

発行所 くろしお出版

〒102-0084 東京都千代田区二番町4-3

Tel: 03-6261-2867　Fax: 03-6261-2879

URL: https://www.9640.jp　Email: kurosio@9640.jp

印　刷 シナノ印刷

ISBN978-4-87424-960-4 C0081